Between the Immensities

Between the Immensities

Doreen Davy

The Book Guild Ltd

First published in Great Britain in 2018 by
The Book Guild Ltd
9 Priory Business Park
Wistow Road, Kibworth
Leicestershire, LE8 0RX
Freephone: 0800 999 2982
www.bookguild.co.uk
Email: info@bookguild.co.uk
Twitter: @bookguild

Typeset in Adobe Garamond Pro

Printed and bound in Great Britain by CPI Group (UK) Ltd, Croydon, CR0 4YY

ISBN 978 1912575 213

British Library Cataloguing in Publication Data.
A catalogue record for this book is available from the British Library.

With love and gratitude to my long-suffering husband Neville – for the copious cups of tea, not to mention the odd glass of wine he brought me while I was writing this novel!

This book is dedicated to the lovely gentle mammy of my childhood.

My Celtic ancestors used to refer to life as 'The Journey Between the Immensities'. The 'immensities' were birth and death. These ancestors observed that the journey wasn't just a straight-line march from cradle to grave. It had an ebb and flow. It had cycles. Sometimes it was like a well choreographed dance where couples moved joyfully in swirling patterns around the floor. This dance of life is our collective journey 'between the immensities'.

Hugh MacDonald

1

All psychologists are mad. The exception, of course, being me. That's how I used to think before I was knocked off my high horse. Before *it* happened. Now I'm not so sure about anything. Things that were once true or false now carry the same question mark. What was black or white has now become a murky grey.

My story begins several years ago during the month of May when I was working as a psychologist on Auckland's North Shore. An ever increasing client workload, combined with petty squabbles and power games amongst senior staff (people expected to be above such behaviour), was making life unnecessarily difficult, and so, for me, a relaxing holiday was long overdue.

As God is supposed to move in mysterious ways, my break away from it all arrived from an unexpected quarter, completely quashing all ideas of sipping cocktails by a pool in Tahiti. I'd been designated the task of returning to my home city of Liverpool to care for my elderly mother who'd been diagnosed with terminal cancer and given only a few months to live. Without any input on my part, my three sisters, all still living in Liverpool, unanimously agreed that I was the ideal person for this role. Given my particular line of work, I was deemed the best equipped to deal with the emotional aspects of such a task.

Of course, there was also the fact I'd been living in New Zealand for many years while my sisters Maureen, Eileen and Colleen had been 'run ragged' looking after Mum. Over time, all the medical appointments, the shopping and the cleaning, the cajoling, the acquiescing and withholding of opinions, not to mention the daily bringing of cakes and tarts, had created a build-up of resentments, so now it was decided that my turn had come. I was to move into Mum's flat and stay with her until it was time for the hospice to take over.

This was not, however, the first time that Mum had been diagnosed with a terminal illness and given just a few months to live. Only last year, my sisters waited while observing the medically predicted downward spiral of our mother's health. And just when everybody was convinced she wouldn't see the week out, when my flight from New Zealand to the UK was booked and priests had been summoned, this amazing old woman rallied forth once more, sitting upright in bed and, with what were supposed to have been her last words, she requested a boiled egg and a slice of buttered Hovis bread, and to make sure the egg was 'runny enough for dipping' but 'not a snot egg'!

Our mother had confounded the medical expertise of the British health system twice before, but this time, I was well assured, it really was six months at best. When people are in their nineties there's an understandable reluctance to perform surgery, therefore a diagnosis can be something of a medical guessing game. So, once again, a flight from Auckland to Manchester was booked. Being resigned to taking on this new role, cocktails in Tahiti would just have to wait.

Given the unusually warm autumn weather in Auckland at that time, you'd think the general populace would have been feeling somewhat content. But that wasn't the case. The phone never seemed to stop ringing as appointments were sought by the anxious, the angry, the confused, the guilty and the depressed. 'The Misery Industry just keeps on booming!' one of my colleagues Mike exclaimed. And he was right. Mike and I worked as part of a team of psychologists specialising in cognitive behaviour therapy (CBT), a therapy which seems to have been the "flavour of the month" for years if not decades.

The day itself seemed like any other Wednesday at work. The clients (who in less politically correct times were called patients) had been scheduled into their one-hour therapy slots. Glossy magazines emphasising the benefits of intermittent dieting, yoga, quinoa and, of course, cognitive behavioural therapy, were piled high on the waiting room table. To avoid any silent awkwardness between them while waiting for their names to be called, tracks of unmemorable music played continuously at low volume. Doors opened and closed accompanied by the usual greetings and farewells. Toilets flushed, kettles boiled and teas and coffees were offered. Behind the consulting room doors, tears fell and noses were blown, problems were discussed and solutions formed, negative thoughts reframed and moods lifted. And on the hour, like the Town Hall clock, the whirring of the EFTPOS machine printed the client's receipt for payment, announcing the end of another therapy session.

But this was no ordinary Wednesday. It was to be my last working day as a psychologist for some time. As the day wore on, the comforting routine of the therapy environment became overwhelmed by a sense of apprehension bordering on dread when I thought of the assignment ahead of me in Liverpool. Have courage, I told myself, you can deal with the situation to the best of your ability at the time. But right now, be here. This moment is your life now.

Marie was my last client for the day, my last official client for that year. As we sat in my consulting room on our separate couches with eyes closed, the only sound to be heard was the ticking of the clock on the wall. The meditation exercise I'd been teaching her involved focusing the mind on the most basic of activities, to simply be aware of your own body breathing in and out. Over the years I'd demonstrated this exercise thousands of times with thousands of clients. Rather than being a monotonous therapeutic procedure, for me it was still one of the perks of the job.

From years of observation I could tell when clients were relaxed enough to begin the next stage, the part involving guided imagery which followed on from the meditation. Marie was definitely in a more relaxed state after just a few minutes of meditating. You can tell if people are relaxed by looking at their feet. If you were to look under a table at an organisational meeting, it's down there on the floor you'd find out what was really going on, because feet talk. That's the place where boredom, excitement, fear and anger are unconsciously expressed.

There was no movement in Marie's feet. No toes turning up, both her feet plonked firmly on the floor indicating a relaxed body. Speaking softly and slowly, I gently entered my client's meditative state to introduce the imagery – 'Marie, I want you to remain in your relaxed state and keep your eyes closed. In your mind I want you to create an image of yourself walking along a white sandy beach on a beautiful summer morning. Feel the warmth of the sun on your shoulders and the cool firm sand beneath your feet. The waves gently break along the shore. As you look up, you notice how blue the sky is. You feel the warm breeze caressing your face and hair. Notice how peaceful you feel, how easily and comfortably your body moves as you walk along the beach. Notice how happy and relaxed you look.' A short silence usually follows this exercise to allow the client to savour their "mind movie".

When Marie finally opened her eyes there were tears, a common emotional response. 'How was that, Marie?'

'Wonderful!' she replied, wiping her face with a tissue.

As Marie's session came to an end, the final session in the course of her therapy, she wished me well for my forthcoming trip back to England. I watched her limp out of the consulting room, back to her life of medication, osteopaths and living with chronic back pain. But now Marie also had strategies for harnessing the mind/body connection via meditation and imagery, exercises that could help with her body's own healing processes.

The psychological industry is an interesting domain. Based on my own observations and experiences in this type of work, it's easy to agree with the commonly held belief that psychologists and psychiatrists (and I suppose you could add counsellors here too) are far more mad than their clients. Could it be that people are attracted to careers in mental health because they were, or in some cases still are, sufferers of emotional disorders themselves? Alternatively, could therapists develop a form of madness via something of a more insidious nature, such as occupational hazard? In other words, could being in contact with anxious and depressed people on a daily basis, week after week, month after month, for years and years carry an element of contagion? Some emotional osmosis at work? At that time, while still in Auckland, I wouldn't have believed that within just a few months it would be me seriously considering my own sanity.

Taking my "Dr Katherine Moore" nameplate down from the consulting room door, it was still hard to believe that this was me, the working class girl – Kathleen Ward – who'd left school at fifteen with no qualifications, her only goals in life being to get married and have children. I often wondered how life would have panned out if I'd never immigrated to New Zealand. But, of course, such wonderings are a waste of time because we can never know.

As my colleagues wished me all the best for the future, part of me began to welcome this opportunity to spend some time caring for the person who gave up so much of her time to look after me as a child. A new episode of my life was about to begin, and on that last day at work I didn't know the magnitude of what lay ahead of me in the Northern Hemisphere. Despite all the years of working in the field of human psychology, the events I was about to experience would prove to be the most amazing of my life so far.

I took one last look at my consulting room, the two matching cream-coloured couches, the wooden coffee table and the all important box of tissues. The large whiteboard where I'd drawn thousands of diagrams in black, red, blue and green to help explain thoughts, emotions, physiology and behaviour. Gently closing the door on this familiar little world, I walked outside to my car, breathing in and savouring the fresh New Zealand air.

Auckland is the largest city in New Zealand with a population of around one and a half million. Compared to cities such as London, New York and Tokyo, Auckland isn't really all that big. It's a sprawling city with two beautiful harbours and a temperate climate which makes it a very desirable place to live. Having two harbours, the Waitemata and the Manukau, means that many people living in Auckland can enjoy the luxury of a sea view from their homes. Interestingly, recent research suggests that when we are old and no longer able to get out and about, it's the view we see from our windows that can provide a psychological benefit to us at that stage of life.

Arriving home from work on that last day at the clinical practice, I walked out on to the back deck of my little cottage to take in the glorious view out across the upper Waitemata Harbour. It's a view I never tired of. Along with the changing colour and movement of the sea, there were often grey herons treading delicately along the shoreline at low tide. At full tide, pods of dolphins sometimes swam up the harbour towards Riverhead. One of the best things about living in such a place is the great sense of oneness it provides with the natural world, something very precious in our modern fast-paced life. And how very different to the block of council flats in Liverpool where I would soon be living.

At that time, the cottage was home to a well behaved little dog called Cindy and to Puzz, a handsome cat with that strong sense of entitlement that only cats seem to have. Both Cindy and Puzz were old. The dog's eyesight and hearing were almost gone and she'd become incontinent. Her appetite, however, was fine and she enjoyed her food as much as ever. When I rang my mum each week, following on from the usual talk about her bowel movements, sore heels, horse racing bets and the weather, she would ask about Cindy – 'How's that poor old dog doing?' They had things in common did Mum and Cindy. Both were in extreme physical decline and approaching death, yet both had fine appetites and derived real pleasure from eating. Cindy was fifteen years old, approximately the same age as my mother in human years.

Cindy's death had to be organised as there was no way I could go off to the UK leaving her in such a state. A date for her euthanasia was set and, when the time came for her to be put down, the experience could only be described as emotional agony. Like a lot of dogs, she'd never enjoyed going to the pet clinic, so when the vet and her assistant arrived at the cottage Cindy immediately recognised the smell on their uniforms. With back legs quivering, she slouched away into the bush to hide. I carried her back on to the deck and, like a traitor, held her down while the needle of death pierced the vein on her front paw. What a terrible thing it was to see the life-light in her eyes switch off, to be instantly replaced with the blankness of dead fish eyes. I buried her body overlooking the harbour where she'd enjoyed many an afternoon sitting in the sun.

If I'd had some sort of faith in an afterlife it might have helped; to have been more like the woman I'd met at the Auckland dog pound when I first came to New Zealand. When I asked her how she could work in such a place, seeing dozens of beautiful unwanted dogs being put down every week, she replied bright and breezily, 'They'll all be back!' Perhaps believing in reincarnation was a necessity in her job.

Preparing to fly to the UK was a sad time. Firstly, because I'd just lost my dearest friend Cindy, only to be followed by a final farewelling of my mother. I only hoped that Puzz would still be alive when I returned. As he was too old to leave long term in a cattery, a house-sitter was organised to look after him. Maggie was a short, middle-aged woman who'd lived as a professional house-sitter all over New Zealand for the last twelve years. I could tell she was a genuine animal lover by the way she said hello to Puzz when she met him and how he responded positively to her gentle stroking of his head.

In my new role caring for Mum, I'd be staying in Bootle, my old home town situated just a few miles north of Liverpool city centre. It's the place where I grew up, where I went to school and where I was married at the ridiculously young age of eighteen. Not surprisingly, this teenage marriage didn't last, but it did produce two lovely children.

Although I'd been back to visit my Liverpudlian family on several occasions in the past, this time would be very different. As well as me caring for my mother during her terminal illness, a special memorial service had been organised to officially acknowledge her status as being the last living survivor of the bombing of a local air-raid shelter in 1941 during the May Blitz of Liverpool. I just hoped she'd last long enough to attend, thereby allowing me the privilege of accompanying her to this important event.

As I prepared for the journey, the idea of being with Mum right up to her last remaining day on earth gained appeal. I wanted to reflect upon where I came from, to be once again amongst my own tribe in my old home town. To enjoy the humour and the music, to reconnect with my ancestral roots. But above all, there was now a growing need to reunite emotionally with my mother before death removed any opportunity to do so.

2

After a one hour delay, the cabin doors of the plane finally closed and the first leg of the long journey to England began. As the plane gathered speed for take-off, I silently farewelled New Zealand. Sitting in a window seat, I looked down at the white clouds below and began to reflect upon my mother and her life. Born in Liverpool during the 1920s, Mum was part of that unfortunate generation who suffered hungry childhood years during the Great Depression only to be followed by the horrors of World War Two. I wondered what it must have been like for her to be married to our dad who was 24 years her senior. From what I could make out, he was a man she'd never felt comfortable being with. She was quite an enigma, my mother. I didn't really know her, as she tended to keep things to herself, especially anything to do with love or personal affection. And now, after all those 91 years, her life was drawing to a close.

It was the youngest of her four girls, Maureen, who'd been her live-in carer for the last few years. Maureen had no husband or children and, living not far from Mum, she became the obvious choice for the role. Mum was adamant she wasn't going into any retirement home, especially since she'd raised four daughters, and if the eldest couldn't look after her because she was so far away in New Zealand, well, there were three others to call upon. The middle daughters Colleen and Eileen helped as best they could even though they were in paid employment. It was Maureen who'd borne the lion's share of responsibility.

As I finished the airline dinner and a second glass of wine, my thoughts continued to drift back in time to our family life in Liverpool. From early on in his marriage, our dad had hoped for a son. He had three Christian names already picked out for his boy, and at the arrival of each of his four daughters, there had been undisguised disappointment. He was Bootle's very own Henry the Eighth in his desperation for a male heir. No doubt his own upbringing contributed to such a mindset, coming as he did from an era when males were generally assumed to be superior to females. And it was because of this patriarchal view that the naming of any baby girls was left to our mother. She chose our names (Kathleen, Colleen, Eileen and Maureen) to keep up the Irish connection with her own background and, unlike the multiple Christian names Dad had picked out for a boy, we girls were christened with only one name each.

Unfortunately for our father, the longed-for William Henry John was never born, his four daughters representing his shameful lack of male virility to the world. Dad sorely resented the fact that we were girls rather than boys, becoming more of a misogynist as the son-less years rolled by. At home, he often seemed to be tired and irritable, which left us, his children, targets for his temper. To him, we were 'peevish bloody bitches' or 'bitches of hell'! Although our father referred to his children in such uncomplimentary terms, none of us bitches seemed to take it at any personal level. Perhaps if within the family environment one of us had been favoured or put on a pedestal as being the "Golden Child" it might have been different. But being all lumped together in the same peevish bitches' camp, these expressions seemed more humorous than anything else.

Like many children of that era, we were sometimes belted by our dad for misbehaving. Mostly it was only on our legs, but a good "leathering" really stung, and for hours after we wore vibrant red stripes across our thin white legs. You didn't have to do anything particularly bad to be punished in this way; merely being full of childish energy manifesting in yelling, jumping about and general exuberance was considered unacceptable in our small house. Dad referred to this behaviour as 'bus-horsing about', and being 'like a bloody bus-horse' often resulted in the leather belt around his waist being frantically unfastened ready for action.

Looking back, our dad would have been in his fifties then and was obviously too old to be bringing up young children, especially as he was raised in a time when children were supposed to be seen but not heard. Our high-pitched childish squeals would have been like torture to his old eardrums. Sometimes when Colleen was given a belting by Dad, in order to make a statement about the unfairness of it all, she'd put a black balaclava over her head back to front so that her face was completely covered. Then she would sit like that for hours on the floor in the corner of the living room not saying a word. This state of martyrdom was known as The Sulking Balaclava!

Soon after the airline staff removed the dinner trays, the lights were turned down and seats were reclined as the long dark part of the journey began. I was now looking forward to seeing my sisters again. To reminisce and laugh together about our childhood days was one of the best aspects of all previous trips back to Liverpool. It was clear from our recollections that none of us really knew Mum that well. Despite her apparent aloofness, there was definitely a certain tenderness shown towards us, this being particularly noticeable whenever we were unwell. Because of this, coming down with mumps or chickenpox was not without benefits, as it often involved bottles of Lucozade and being allowed to lie in our parents' big bed all day where the special mothering attention took place. Looking back, it's little wonder that we girls all used to enjoy being sick!

Although she tried to protect us as much as possible from Dad's beltings, Mum's appeals for leniency were usually ignored. As a child she'd witnessed her own mother being regularly beaten by her father, but we never saw Dad hit our mum. However, regardless of the beltings and him calling us bitches and bus-horses, somewhere deep inside our dad was a kind heart. After dishing out a hiding he always brought us sweets and chocolates home the following evening and a box of Milk Tray for Mum, so he obviously felt some sense of remorse.

Like most parents of that era, expressing love verbally towards your children, or to anybody come to that, was not the done thing. Ironically though, love was everywhere, as that was the name given to people in general. From the milkman who left the bottles of fresh milk on the doorstep each morning to the woman behind the counter in the corner shop, everybody was called "Love". But you didn't hear any expressions such as 'I love you', as it was via actions that love was revealed. For example, seeing our mother standing by the school gate in the pouring rain with our raincoats (or macs as we called them) at 4pm when school finished. I suppose you could say it was just maternal instinct, the thing that mothers naturally did to help their children. But not all mothers did this. Some children were soaked walking home alone in heavy rain, their mothers preoccupied at the local bingo hall or betting shop.

* * *

At last the lights on the plane were turned back on and tongs of steaming hand-towels were distributed and collected before the long awaited breakfast trays arrived. After a short stop in Singapore, I boarded another plane for the second leg of the journey to the UK. This time I had an aisle seat but, as with the first flight, I didn't get a decent sleep. The best I could manage were short dozes in between watching films, eating, drinking and general fidgeting. Eventually the plane was flying over England heading towards Manchester. A shiver of excitement shot through me as I tried to squeeze my swollen feet back into my shoes, knowing that very soon

I'd be seeing my family again. I even relished the idea of moving in with Mum and looking after her as though it had always been my destiny.

Eileen and Colleen were there to meet me at Manchester airport. After some awkward sisterly hugs, the banter and nervous giggling began. There seemed to be this unspoken family rule that our interactions would mainly involve creating laughter. Anger was permitted as long as there was some element of comedy to it, but tears of sadness were taboo. We grew up outwardly conveying an emotional staunchness, avoiding any display of the softer emotions such as love or sadness, a behaviour largely learned from the main role model, our mother. Over the years, when going through a painful or even heart-breaking time, keeping up an appearance of hardiness via the use of comedy had become the norm. Eileen was the queen of this particular and somewhat unhealthy approach to life. It did, however, create a most unusual sense of humour. A humour capable of providing the type of laughter known as "roaring", when bodies hunch over, breathing becomes difficult, faces are contorted, with eyes streaming and the voice gagged. Physically, it's akin to an internal workout which leaves you feeling exhausted but at the same time provides healthy benefits. The only time I have a good roar is in Liverpool with my family, the gist of the comedy often being lost on others.

Walking out of the airport between my two sisters, the most obvious topic for banter was physical appearance, given it had been over three years since we'd last met. Thus, the signs of aging were exaggerated for laughs. Eileen looked at me with her head cocked to one side while biting her lower lip, the half smile and furrowed brows indicating mock concern. I knew what was coming next.

'A lot more lines this time… Oh God, what's happened to your neck?'

Her eyes moved from my neck to my face and down again in wonder. According to Eileen, as we "turn to seed" our necks become either scraggy turkey-gobblers or fat jolly wobblers. Gobblers or wobblers. One or the other.

'A fine gobbler coming along nicely,' she concluded.

A more sensitive person might find this type of teasing upsetting or even cruel, but this was the way things had been all our lives. The aim is to create laughter rather than upset, an opportunity to laugh along with others at yourself. Just in case there was now any uncertainty as to how I might take Eileen's remarks, the ever considerate Colleen removed her scarf, offering her own neck for inspection.

'Look at this wobbler I've got here!' she said, puffing her cheeks out like a bullfrog for effect. 'A big goitre ready to burst!'

Although Colleen had a bit of fat under her chin, this deliberate exaggeration exercised the imagination to such an absurd extent that laughter was the only possible response.

Each Christmas and birthday, year after year, my sisters sent me the same present by post – wrinkle cream! Each year these anti-aging creams promised "miracle recovery" as they became "more intense" with "ultra replenishing" and "double action age repair". Competing with each other, Eileen and Colleen went shopping in search of new descriptive heights for my creamy presents. Needless to say, none of the products made any difference, but I enjoyed the joke.

Moving on from aging necks, Eileen spotted the name tag on one of my suitcases, resulting in a bout of eye-rolling and tut-tutting. Instead of Kathleen I'd put the name Katherine, with the preceding title of Dr which came with the PhD I'd completed in psychology some years ago. When I moved from Liverpool to New Zealand, it presented an opportunity to change my name. Kathleen is such an old name you now only see it in the Death columns of local newspapers.

According to my sisters, Kathleen conjures up a working class barmaid of the 1950s, the type of character you'd see in those old black and white films. Clearly, I'd taken their observations on board, choosing a new name for a new beginning. Although my family knew I called myself Katherine, this new identity was treated with a humorous type of contempt. Pointing to the Dr title on the nametag, Eileen said in an exaggerated and loud Liverpudlian accent – 'Eh, our Ka-leen, what's all this, then?'

Were they in any way proud of me and what I'd achieved given our working class background? Probably not. In fact, completing a PhD in psychology and using the Dr title was more likely to be interpreted as showing off or one-upmanship. It was a bit like the old "Crabs in a Bucket" story. Apparently, if you put a load of live crabs in a bucket, no lid is required, because those trying to climb out are pulled back down by the others. This crab, however, had made it out, but it seemed there was a price to pay for doing so.

As well as having little regard for academic qualifications, nobody in my family placed value on anything associated with psychology. To them, counselling therapy was an over-priced indulgence for the weak or bored. Out-dated stereotypical images were held involving neurotic people lying on couches talking about their mothers for years while therapists sat on chairs stroking their beards and nodding. So no, the wares I peddled were not well regarded, not at that time anyway.

Once in Eileen's car and on the motorway heading towards Liverpool, the topic turned to our mother's situation. How frail she was, how over these last few months she'd become even more negative and cantankerous. Hoping to create a laugh, Eileen turned to the usual stories, which involved impersonating Mum and her morbid preoccupation with bowel movements. She described a recent incident which involved her taking Mum to the hospital, and how in the waiting room Mum told everybody there how she hadn't been for ten days and how it was 'terrible uncomfortable to sit on all that lot'! When Mum's name was finally called out by a nurse, she shuffled in to see the doctor with one hand on her bottom as though keeping a lid on it.

Eileen got the laugh she was after, but I felt sorry for Mum, having to suffer like that. On the other hand, it was the sort of story Mum herself would enjoy hearing, perhaps not on that day at the hospital but at a later date, and which would no doubt provide her with a good laugh, especially in the way Eileen could dramatise it. As she became older, Mum's obsession with her bowels had intensified. It was the same old problem of constipation and discomfort. From as far back as I can remember, she'd been like this, and for her now to have a medical diagnosis of bowel cancer seemed to be life's final insult.

Continuing our conversation about Mum, Eileen warned me, with a tiny smirk that was meant to be noticed, 'Poor Maureen's been run ragged with her non-stop demands.'

'Well, I'm not expecting any of it to be easy.'

'We can assure you that it won't be,' Eileen said, shaking her head from side to side to emphasise the hopelessness of the situation. With a throaty little half-laugh she gave me a further warning – 'You don't know what you're letting yourself in for. You're like a babe in the woods.' I marvelled at how easily she could overlook the fact that I'd been summoned to take on this new role by Eileen herself along with my other sisters. I hadn't actively sought it. But that was Eileen's humour, trying to wind me up for a bit of comedy.

It wasn't long after Maureen moved in with Mum that she became Poor Maureen. I could imagine how very soon that same adjective would be applied to me too, perhaps with an extra middle bit thrown in – Poor Old Kathleen. My intention was to manage each day to the best of my ability at that time, advice I'd often given to clients who were chronic worriers. However, the description of me being a babe in the woods would soon prove accurate.

Eileen insisted on driving with the windows down and no heating on in the car, enjoying the cold air on her face as she drove. Colleen was obviously aware of her sister's need for fresh air as she was well dressed for it, wearing a scarf and a woollen coat while I shivered in my light summer clothes.

So there I was back in my homeland. Small stabs of

nostalgia pricked at my heart as we travelled along the motorway. Seeing the big signposts coming up saying BOOTLE brought back fleeting memories of times gone by. Times when I was a child, the teenage girl obsessed by The Beatles, the bored office worker, the wife, the young mother. All those stages of life buried under the heavy weight of time. Gerry Marsden's voice suddenly began singing 'Ferry Cross the Mersey' as we drove past the Pier Head. It was a CD track Eileen had specifically prepared to play at that moment to go with the scenery. It certainly added to the poignancy of my homecoming.

As we passed a block of shops, I suggested stopping to buy flowers for Mum.

'Ooh, God, she wouldn't thank you for that,' Colleen advised, recounting the negative response she'd received when she'd bought flowers for Mother's Day last year. How she was told in no uncertain terms – 'Yer shouldn't have wasted yer money' and to 'Take them away!' Like Eileen, Colleen could do a good take-off of Mum's voice and mannerisms, which was hard not to find amusing. Impersonation was all part of the humour. Based on what I'd heard about Mum's aversion to flowers, I didn't buy any. She certainly sounded as though she'd become more crotchety, but to my idealistic mind she would always be the lovely gentle mammy of my childhood.

3

Soon we were driving into the car park near the high-rise block of flats in Marsh Lane where Mum lived. A gusty cold wind was blowing in from the docks, bringing with it the salty smell of the River Mersey. Shuffling into the lift on the building's ground floor, my sisters and I along with all the luggage managed to fill the entire space.

As the lift began moving upwards, there was a tightening sensation in my chest accompanied by an accelerating heart rate, both physical symptoms of anxiety. I certainly had no phobia of lifts, but there was a strong sense of mounting tension. Tears were already welling up in my eyes and a choking lump of sadness lodged in my throat. Previous visits had always carried the question of will I ever see *her* again once I leave, this woman we once called our mammy, the same person who'd been there for us right throughout our childhood years. This underlying question always made the journey back to New Zealand a heart-breaking experience. But this time I knew the answer. I'd never see my mother again once I left England, and already that sense of loss was physically manifesting within me.

Not wanting my sisters to see me in such an emotionally crumbling state, especially when claiming to be a trained psychologist specialising in how to change your emotions by changing the way you think, I quickly focused my mind on the external environment and away from the internal drama. Drawing on my psychological "bag of tools", I became very mindful of being in the lift, noticing all the details of my immediate surroundings as though my life depended on it. I also reminded myself that right now in this moment, Mum was still alive and so was I. Both of us still here amongst the living.

In the lift there was a definite smell of stale urine overlaid by a hint of disinfectant. Eileen and Colleen held their noses, their usual coping mechanism when using this lift. As the doors opened on to the seventh floor, a new smell resembling boiled cabbage greeted us. These flats housed pensioners, most of the occupants coming from an era when boiled cabbage was very popular. Opposite the lift was a white door, the flat where Mum had lived for the last 28 years. The door was unlocked, so, after a quick knock and the usual greeting, which involved Eileen and then Colleen calling out 'Are you up, Billy?' in a man's voice, we all shuffled inside.

To explain this unusual greeting, it was on a late afternoon many years ago that a drunken man began shouting, 'Are you up, Billy?' through the door's open letter box of our terraced house in Canal Street. The man had obviously mistaken our house as being where somebody he knew by the name of Billy lived, and he called that same question over and over, his loud voice yelling down our lobby. At the end of the lobby near the staircase stood my mum and her four girls, all staring at what we could see of this fellow's unattractive mouth calling through the opened oblong slot. He was all whiskery with rotten teeth and a strong smell of alcohol on his breath – 'ARE YOU UP, BILLY?' Eventually Mum opened the door and told him there were no Billys living there and that he should try some other house. We never found out who the lazy Billy was supposed to be, and the whiskery mouth never came back. But over the years the voice and the call became the greeting when entering Mum's home. It often made her laugh, so that alone made this strange ritual worth continuing.

We entered the lounge area, where Mum was sitting in her armchair, her hands folded on her lap, looking a bit like *Whistler's Mother* minus the bonnet. She seemed much smaller and thinner now, her hair more grey and wispy than it had been when I'd seen her last. Slowly turning her head in our direction as the luggage was trundled in, her hazel eyes came to rest upon me. It was always hard to know what to say in these situations. I stooped down beside her chair and kissed her forehead. 'Hello, Mum, I've finally arrived.'

She acknowledged my arrival with a small nod before asking how the flight was.

Her voice was small and low but it was that same voice from my childhood. My lovely mammy's voice.

'Long. It seemed a lot longer flight this time.'

The conversation quickly turned to more everyday

stuff as Mum looked at her other daughters and began complaining about the noise of the workmen outside fixing the road. I suppose my kissing her felt awkward and she wanted to quickly return to something more familiar. Maureen came out of the kitchen wiping her hands on a tea-towel. As usual, she kept her distance and avoided eye contact as though she was shy of me. Like Mum, she didn't seem to want any physical contact, so after a quick hello she put the kettle on and busied herself preparing sandwiches in the safety of the kitchen.

When the complaining about the roadworks finally ran out, I knelt down again by Mum's chair and asked her how she was. The others smirked at each other knowingly. I might have guessed the answer coming. It was all about her bowels. The same problems I'd heard hundreds of times over the phone. Without realising it, I placed my hand gently on the back of her bony little hand. A natural gesture demonstrating care.

'Oh God, don't touch that!' she cried. Her frail voice now shrill and urgent as she pulled her hand away.

'She's got a sore scab on that hand,' Maureen informed me as she carried in a plate of sandwiches. I quickly apologised for the clumsy attempt at physical affection.

'Sorry, Mum, I didn't know.'

It was hard not to feel stupid, especially as Eileen and Colleen were now roaring with laughter. Mum looked at me and then at the others laughing before joining in the giggling. Maureen also allowed herself a bit of a suppressed chuckle. The entertainment had begun. As soon as anybody began to behave as though we were ordinary and mainstream, the situation suddenly backfired, highlighting an absurd response rather than what might be considered the norm. This was the essence of the humour; almost everything about us seemed to be out of the ordinary in a negative kind of way. We were like players on a stage reading from this bizarre script which had become our life.

After the lunch (which was called dinner), Colleen and Eileen hurried off, shouting 'Good luck' as they disappeared down the lift back to their own lives, while Maureen was all animation and avoidance, readying herself to leave Mum's flat and shift into the new place she'd be renting in Seaforth. When finally saying 'Tara' to us, Maureen appeared the most enthusiastic I'd ever seen her, obviously looking forward to her new life, glad to be finally passing the responsibility of our mother on to somebody else.

From here on, it would be just me and Mum. I was determined to make a positive connection with this woman whom I really felt a lot of love for, but how do you go about cuddling a porcupine or interact at a deeper level with somebody who just wants to talk about their bowel movements? My plan was to take a very pragmatic approach to being able to touch her, by mentioning how scientific studies indicate there are both physical and emotional benefits from simply touching and being touched. That touch can decrease the heart rate, the blood pressure and the stress hormone cortisol. Surely that would be enough to allow me to be physically affectionate towards my own mother. I also knew that touch could increase levels of oxytocin, the hormone responsible for triggering feelings of love. You can always love somebody without it having to be reciprocated; it's just nicer when the feeling is mutual. However, I wasn't counting on it!

As for getting Mum to open up and interact at a deeper level, I decided to play that one by ear. I knew that older people usually enjoyed talking about the past, so maybe just talking about days gone by would be a good place to start. Both myself and Mum had a lot of learning ahead of us, and you could say that in our own ways at that particular point in time we were both babes in the wood.

Feeling jet-lagged and with fatigue pressing heavily on my eyelids, I knew from experience that it wasn't good to lie down for a postprandial nap, even though every cell in my body was wanting exactly that. A coma; that's what a nap would turn into given how tired I was. Mum was already lying back in her reclining chair getting herself ready for an afternoon sleep. The time was 1pm, so I guessed that that was part of her routine regardless of my presence. I would have to wait until evening before closing my eyes and falling into a deep and much needed sleep.

While Mum was having her nap, I studied her, in the security of knowing I was alone and that my gaze wouldn't be interrupted. In many ways I idealised her. To me, her face still resembled one of those ancient Greek marble statues with her perfectly straight classical nose. I saw her in the goddess Athena, in the Statue of Liberty and in Botticelli's Venus. They all had my mother's classically beautiful face. But of course, with all her faults and frailties, Mum was only human. She could be narrow-minded, bigoted and insensitive at times. As she slept, her head fell to one side and her mouth opened slightly, discouraging me from any further intensive study.

Turning my attention elsewhere, I looked around the lounge. On one wall hung the New Zealand calendar I'd sent her for Christmas, the current month's picture showing the alpine grandeur of the Southern Alps. On the opposite wall, in stark contrast to New Zealand's natural splendour, hung a Liverpool calendar displaying the city's beautiful Neoclassical-styled St George's Hall. Looking down at the lounge floor, I noticed that Mum now had a new carpet. It was all brown and beige whorls with sprinklings of dark red, the type of patterned carpet older people tend to prefer, usually for reasons of practicality. The lounge suite was the same light brown draylon couch and two armchairs she'd bought second-hand about 20 years ago, still complemented by a couple of beige velvet scatter cushions and matching curtains. It all looked quite dull but in a little brown hen cosy sort of way, the grandiose images on the calendars adding a touch of counterpoint to the drabness of the room.

On the coffee table was an accumulation of newspapers and magazines, the most recent editions lying on top, along with an assortment of medications and ointments. A sideboard with glass sliding doors displayed a crockery set which I didn't think had ever been used. Next to this were her best glasses and a few little ornaments of dogs and cats, mementos of other people's holidays. Framed pictures dominated the top of the sideboard – mainly photos of us girls when we were children, alongside photos of our children. Mum's four grandsons with their toothy smiles and inherited cowlicks looked back at me. I felt my heart move as I looked at my own two little boys. The other two boys were Colleen's lads. All four of them were now grown men living in different countries. My elder son had moved to the Netherlands, while the younger one had settled in Australia. Colleen's sons were also living in Australia – the so-called Lucky Country. It wasn't how we imagined things would be, but then I don't suppose Mum ever imagined losing her eldest daughter to New Zealand.

Bundled behind one of the framed photos was the last lot of Mother's Day cards from her daughters. Among them was a Get Well Soon card, a scribbled message saying – *Hope your Vesuvius settles down soon, and all best wishes for a speedy recovery for your sore heel, your itchy neck, ingrown toenail and the scab on your hand, oh and also your bowels and bedsore.* It was obviously meant to be a joke, no doubt thought up by my sisters to create a laugh for Mum. Mum had an abscess on her appendix which intermittently "exploded", leaking foul-smelling fluid from her side, hence its name Vesuvius. She was considered too old to undergo surgery so had to manage as best she could with antibiotics and dressings. I remember her telling me on the phone, with a hint of pride in her voice, that Elton John suffered from the same ailment, but of course with him being younger he was able to have the problem treated surgically. I put the Get Well card on the table in the hope of providing her with a fresh laugh when she woke up.

Moving on from the lounge, I had a look in the bedroom that was now to be mine. The old wooden wardrobe was much smaller than I remembered it. How strange it felt hanging my adult clothes in this little wardrobe of my childhood, as though I was attempting to travel back in time. There was still the pungent smell of mothballs – those little white toxic-smelling balls that people once used to deter moths from destroying their clothes. Vague feelings of nostalgia were triggered by the noxious smell.

When we were children, this wardrobe was a magical and secret place. It was where the Christmas presents were hidden, a place where Colleen and I spent many an hour crouched down below the hanging garments pretending to be camping. We'd never been camping but thought sitting in a wardrobe might be similar to being in a tent. When we closed the wardrobe door, and sat cross legged in the pitch dark, a new world emerged via our whispering dialogue. There were no concerns about claustrophobia then, even with the toxic mothball fumes. That small confined place provided a setting for our imaginations to soar.

Along with the wardrobe and the narrow single bed (which at that jet-lagged moment looked devastatingly alluring), there was our old wooden dressing table with the three mirrors. Sitting at the dressing table, you could see yourself from both sides as well as the front view, and with five females in the house those mirrors were well used!

As children, for some strange reason, we believed that getting your face soaked with rain made you beautiful, so whenever there was a heavy downpour we'd be pushing and jockeying for the best position to hang our heads out of the narrow kitchen door into the backyard. By holding our upturned faces to the sky, the beautifying cold rain would drench our heads while our bodies stayed dry inside. Once thoroughly saturated, we'd dash upstairs to the dressing table mirrors to assess how gorgeous we'd become. Looking back as an adult, I marvelled at our naivety, wondering from where in our imaginations did we derive such ideas. Perhaps it was seeing how beautiful Audrey Hepburn looked in the rain scenes from *Breakfast at Tiffany's,* a film Mum had taken us to see at the local Bank Hall picture theatre.

The bedroom bore no evidence of Maureen's recent presence apart from a list of procedures she'd left me, as though Mum were some idiosyncratic kitchen appliance that required detailed instructions. Amongst other things, the list itemised everything I needed to know about Mum's dietary schedule: the specific times when she was to have breakfast, morning tea, lunch, afternoon tea, evening tea (what we called dinner in New Zealand) and supper. As well as stipulated times for the six culinary events of the day, the days of the week determined what would be on the plates and in the cups at those times. For example, the Monday evening meal was a boiled egg and buttered bread, Tuesday's meal was a sausage complemented by a tinned tomato, and so on. No wonder Mum and Maureen looked so thin; but thinking back to our childhood days, a boiled egg and a slice of bread was often a main meal.

Mum had lived through a hungry childhood during the 1930s, so for her this type of eating was the norm, and she'd continued living with a scarcity consciousness throughout the later decades of relative abundance. Our dad used to be presented with a pitifully meagre main meal after a full day's physically demanding work on the docks. He never said anything but, thinking back, he must have had a good feed of something else before coming home, otherwise he wouldn't have been able to work as hard as he did. There were plenty of little cafés and chippys along Bootle's Dock Road so hopefully he enjoyed a plate of chips before coming home for his sausage or egg.

Like Mum, Dad also seemed to be a lover of routine. He'd come home from work, take off his cap, jacket and bicycle clips and, after spending a while in the lavatory at the end of the backyard, he'd come into the house to wash his hands and face in the kitchen sink. Then, looking all important as the man of the house, he'd sit upright at the head of the table waiting for Mum to present him with his tiny meal.

There wasn't a lot of conversation between my parents; however, one of the main topics of their scant dialogue tended to revolve around toileting. While munching his meal he would inquire about his wife's bowel movements.

'Have you had any luck today, Mammy?' He always called her Mammy when we were there. In response, Mum would often shake her head and crinkle her nose as she answered, 'No, not much luck today.' Colleen once earned a clip round the ear from Dad for cheekily commenting on Mum's answer about not having much luck.

'Oh, such hard luck, Mammy!' she said with a feigned sympathetic expression, pushing her own luck while we girls laughed. She only did it the once.

For my parents, bowel movements were all about luck and had nothing to do with diet or lifestyle. There was always a variety of laxatives, such as Syrup of Figs or Milk of Magnesia, readily at hand on the sideboard for when their luck ran out completely. Other people living in the neighbourhood must have suffered similar problems as there was always plenty of talk about who was undergoing a haemorrhoid operation that week. Following on from the war years, the 1950s in North West England seemed to have been the decade of constipation as well as the era that spawned the generation known as the Baby Boomers!

This lack of recognising a connection between diet and physical consequences was a bit like smoking. Just about every adult in our street smoked, my mum being one of the few exceptions. Puffing on a cigarette in those days was not linked to damaging your lungs, so for most men and women it was just as routine as having a cup of tea.

I decided to ignore Maureen's list of culinary rules. Times had changed and there was no need for Mum to continue living like that. It was a Friday afternoon so, looking at the list, we were scheduled to have two fishfingers, mashed potato and butterbeans for tea – one of the same evening meals we used to have as children. I decided that in the morning I'd take Mum to the local Asda supermarket in her wheelchair and introduce her to all the marvellous food she could have while I was looking after her – fresh salmon, New Zealand lamb, chicken breasts stuffed with camembert cheese. She might not have long to live, but while on my watch she'd eat well.

Walking into the kitchen I tossed Maureen's list into the rubbish bin. There on the bench, sulking under a paper bag, were four soggy looking fishfingers. Yes, it was Friday all right. Even if all I provided was a more interesting diet for the remainder of Mum's life, then my trip would be worthwhile. But I wanted so much more for her than that.

I wanted to provide her with the opportunity to open up. To get to know her, adult to adult. To form a very special therapeutic alliance!

When Mum woke from her nap, she looked a bit confused when she saw me and not Maureen sitting there in her lounge.

'Did you have a nice sleep, Mum?'

She gave a little nod. After helping her to the toilet and then back to her armchair, I picked up the Get Well Soon card.

'I found this on the sideboard. I bet it's from Eileen, isn't it?'

She couldn't see what I had, so I brought it up closer for her to read while she put her glasses on.

'It was from the three of them,' she said, handing it back to me. 'It gave me a good laugh.' I read the message out loud for her, which produced the smile I'd been hoping for.

'You know what, though, they forgot the macular degeneration in me eye,' she said, pointing to her left eye as though she'd been short-changed.

'Shall I add macular degeneration to the card?' I suggested, picking up a pen from the coffee table.

'No, put it away,' she said looking at the clock, 'Julie'll be here soon.'

Julie was the nurse who came every second day to check on Mum, to change her dressings and to make sure she was taking her medications.

'She's a nice girl Julie; you'll like her.'

Julie arrived on the dot at 2pm, and yes she was very likeable. Mum became a different person for her, like an obedient child at school who wanted to please the teacher. The nurse only stayed for about fifteen minutes before leaving to visit her next elderly patient who happened to live in the same block of flats.

About an hour later on that same Friday afternoon, I learned just how much Routine and Habit were totally controlled by Time. It wasn't until the clock on the mantelpiece showed 3pm that the kettle was allowed to be filled for our afternoon cup of tea accompanied by an Eccles cake. Mum was determined that this was how things had to be. So when I began to fill the kettle at 2.50pm this was interpreted as an act of mutiny. Gesturing her authority with an outstretched hand and raising her voice, and with an ever watchful eye on the clock, she ordered me not to go near that kettle until exactly 3pm.

This bizarre regimented existence in Mum's flat must have been allowed to take root and flourish over the last few years until it became a god-given rule of the universe. What time you ate or drank and what you consumed were dictated by the calendar and the clock in joint governance. Maureen must have taken the path of least resistance by acquiescing to Mum's fierce insistence on routine, and although the days of the week often conveyed what we had for tea when we were children, she had never been this fanatical over the time on the clock.

As a psychologist I'd worked with obsessive clients but none quite as "anal" as what I'd just encountered. I should have guessed from my New Zealand phone calls to Mum that something wasn't quite right. If I rang her a few minutes before our usual time I was told to ring back at the exact agreed time. I assumed it must have been because *Coronation Street* was still on. If I rang her in the mornings and my timing was a bit out, I was told she couldn't talk then because it was the time she had her wash, or that the kettle had just been switched on for tea, so could I ring back in half an hour. God forbid she would switch a kettle off to talk to her daughter in New Zealand! I used to take this sort of thing personally, believing that she was angry with me for moving so far away from Liverpool, but it was simply that she'd become a slave to a routine dictated by the clock.

In the lounge, the round black clock sat majestically on the mantelpiece like an overlord surveying his little domestic kingdom. Its large black hand crept slowly and steadily around its face, while the thin red hand, moving on a faster orbit, ticked away each second. With all this movement condensed into such a small area, the clock seemed to take on an irrepressible life of its own. It wasn't just a participant in this regulating theatre playing out in Mum's flat, it was the key player.

When people feel as though they've lost control of their lives, a sense of regaining that control is sometimes created by engaging in certain obsessive behaviours. It's well known that routine can offer a comforting sense of continuity, especially for the elderly. This seems to have been what had happened with Mum. Perhaps she'd been feeling vulnerable, given her increasing physical frailty combined with a fear of approaching death. Such feelings can make life seem out of control, and her rigid timetable probably provided some sense of order.

Putting the kettle down as directed, I meekly went back to my seat while Master Clock tick-tocked his indomitable presence. I knew what I had to do, but not until tomorrow, not until after I'd had a good long sleep.

4

Although I was the eldest and had reigned supreme over my sisters during childhood, in our teenage years the pecking order changed as Eileen, the third daughter who used to be the quiet one, developed into the more dominant personality. Being tall with black hair, Eileen's eyes were a bright cornflower blue, quite unlike her three dark-eyed, mousey haired sisters. Nobody else in the family had such blue eyes except for an old granddad on our father's side named Albert. This granddad had snow white hair, a clipped neat little moustache (known as a muzzy) and watery blue eyes which he always seemed to be dabbing with a handkerchief. According to family lore, the young Albert had gained a reputation for being a gambler and a ladies' man, but there wasn't a hint of such notoriety when he paid his annual visit to our house. He sometimes wore a carnation in his lapel, though, along with a fedora hat instead of the flat cap most working class men wore then. So, in some ways you could say he looked more of a dandy than your average old man.

This grand old granddad had a strange habit of drinking his tea from a saucer rather than from his cup and, as we didn't get many visitors, we girls gathered round him watching this eccentric behaviour with intense interest. At the end of each visit, while fumbling to put a wet handkerchief in his pocket, Albert gave us each a stale Mars Bar. They were always stale but we ate them with gusto anyway. He was such a very old man, a relic from a by-gone era tottering about with the aid of a walking stick, his overcoat pockets laden down with stale Mars Bars and wet hankies.

Yes, Eileen had definitely inherited her grandfather's eyes and, although we never knew the younger Albert and never witnessed any roguish behaviour, we could see something of an impulsive nature in Eileen. A bit like Mum at times, there was a theatrical element to Eileen's personality and it was no surprise to anybody when she joined a local amateur dramatic group. She enjoyed relaying all the petty histrionic behaviour and rivalry that went on between the actors, who seemed to create far more drama backstage than anything they performed for an audience. Eileen also enjoyed everything to do with music – singing, playing the piano and dancing. She had an excellent ear, which made her a very good impersonator, and a good singer and pianist. It was sometimes hard to know who the real Eileen was, as she played her various personas so well.

My other sister Colleen was younger than me by just eleven months and as children we were sometimes mistaken for twins. Being positioned between Eileen and me, Colleen developed the typical middle-child trait of being the pleaser and peace-maker rather than manoeuvring for a position of sibling power, often taking the role of referee when Eileen began to assert herself and the pinching, hair-pulling and slapping began. Of all Mum's daughters, Colleen was the most domesticated. She liked to keep a tidy house and a fridge perpetually filled with cakes and chocolates should anybody drop by for a visit. At times, her kind nature could be a problem as there were those who took advantage of her generosity. Even the neighbourhood cats (the strays as well as the homed) recognised the alluring combination of a full pantry and a kind heart, resulting in an assortment of opportunistic moggies hanging about Colleen's front and back gardens all year round.

And then there was Maureen. The sensitive pixie-faced little girl who came into the family when I was ten, Colleen nine and Eileen eight. The sibling landscape was already well established by then, and because of the age gap Maureen never fully became part of it. She was always too young. Maureen's arrival was totally unexpected – not that any of us were planned – and our mother had no qualms in declaring how four children was one too many. In a lot of ways, Maureen's childhood was like that of an only child. I was working when she started school, and at that time Colleen, Eileen and I were far more interested in The Beatles and The Rolling Stones than anything to do with our little sister.

Our father died not long after Maureen was born, which left Mum a young widow with four children. Being part of an all female family was mostly a lot of fun and good laughs. Our mother seemed to blossom with the new found freedom of having no husband, this particular phenomenon being aptly named Widow's Bloom. In many ways, during that time Mum became more like a big sister than a mother. She loved The Beatles and the other Merseyside artists who took over the music charts during the '60s. She would sing along to their songs on the radio, sometimes even breaking into a spontaneous little dance as she sang. It was a happy time to be alive. But, like Eileen, our mother had a very private side to her, a part that remained hidden just below the surface.

I wondered how I would bring up the cancer diagnosis with her and how she would respond. But it was too soon for me to tackle that. I needed to get over my jet-lag first.

Along with introducing Mum to delicious food, for the remaining part of her life I wanted us both to experience a close mother/daughter relationship. But to do that, I'd need to penetrate that guard she usually put up to contain her private world. Although I was a trained therapist, I was about to meet one of my most difficult clients. My mother!

* * *

The next morning, while having our tea and toast together, the subject of food and the importance of eating a good balanced diet was raised. Apparently Eileen had told Mum that I was a health freak and upon hearing this she'd insisted on buying a tin of baby carrots just for me.

'Ooh, I take healthy living very seriously,' she said while nibbling on a piece of toast with her two remaining teeth, one upper left, the other lower right; her other teeth no doubt casualties of a thousand jam tarts.

'Just look in that fridge; it's full of good healthy food!' she assured me. 'I even drink orange juice every day for vitamin C. I've always looked after meself well.'

What could I say to that? Peering into the fridge there didn't seem to be much of anything.

'I can't see any orange juice in here, Mum; you must have run out of it.'

'No, I haven't run out of it,' she said, a slight irritation rising in her voice. 'It's in there, next to the milk on the shelf in the door.'

She was now up out of her chair shuffling precariously towards the kitchen. In the open fridge she pointed to a half empty bottle of Fanta. The right side of her upper lip was curling, which caused her nose to crinkle, a sure sign she was becoming frustrated with her obviously stupid daughter.

'It's there! Looking at yer!'

The quality of her vitamin C intake didn't seem worth debating so we finished our breakfast in silence.

Once the two regular carers (Laura and Brenda) from the local agency left after completing their daily half-hour routine of washing and dressing Mum, I suggested we take an outing to the local Asda supermarket. As the weather that morning was fine and the supermarket was only a short distance from her flat, Mum agreed to come with me. To say it took a long time for her to get ready would be an understatement. Firstly, she wanted to finish studying the racing pages of *The Sun,* trying to pick the winners in the afternoon's horse-racing on TV. After writing out her bets, she changed her socks and smoothed Oil of Olay on her face and neck in slow motion. In between combing her hair, she spent some time meticulously removing individual hairs from the fingers of the comb and carefully placing them one at a time into the rubbish basket next to her chair. This was done with such deliberation and precision you'd think she was defusing a bomb. Her tongue was slightly out between her lips as she fully concentrated on the task, completely oblivious to me waiting there in my coat with the wheelchair unfolded ready for her.

After about 20 minutes of hair removal, she had one last look at the comb before putting it away. Being patient with people, especially the elderly and young children, is akin to practising acts of kindness, something I aimed to become good at.

Being patient, however, was really put to the test some years ago at Mum's birthday party. Just as we were about to have a celebratory toast, she continued telling somebody about the day her appendix bag burst, providing a full description of the spillage and how it's 'such a terrible thing being this old'. She hadn't noticed everybody waiting with their glasses of bubbly going flat and the lit candles on the cake nearing the end of their wicks. We all waited for her to finish her conversation without interrupting. A collective act of kindness.

Finally buttoning up her coat and tying the tartan scarf she liked to wear around her head, Mum was ready to go out. I was patient. This was my mammy and she was now very old. Pushing her in the wheelchair I carefully navigated the curbs and pot-holes along the way to the supermarket. Mum gave me directions via her index finger and a faint 'Here' or 'This way' accompanied by a slight nod of her head even though I knew the way. I just acquiesced to all these little behaviours, which at times could be annoying but were likely to contribute to some sense of continuing importance in the world for her. She'd always placed a high value on her independence and for her now to be in a wheelchair at the mercy of others must have been hard. To help her maintain some feeling of prominence, for the last few years I'd posted photos from New Zealand to Mum so that she could be in charge of showing them to the others, even though it would have been so much easier to simply email them as attachments to Eileen.

Just as we were going into the supermarket, Mum pointed to a woman in a red coat who walked past us pushing a loaded trolley.

'That's Julie-Ann Jones, the girl who was in your class at Saint Mary's,' she said in a low voice. 'Do yer wanna say hello to her?'

I did not. I remembered that girl all right, but this middle-aged woman with short brown hair bore no resemblance to the Julie-Ann of my childhood. At home, there was never any sense of being deprived, even with three younger sisters and a lot of squabbling going on. But at primary school it was different. It was there I suffered an acute sense of deprivation and envy thanks to Julie-Ann. It wasn't what she did, it was simply how she looked. Fascination mingled with covetousness came to life when I gazed in awe at her angora cardigans, short-sleeved in summer and long-sleeved in winter, all lovingly hand-knitted by Julie-Ann's mother, a different pastel shade for each day of the week. So, if Julie-Ann was wearing pale pink, then you knew it was Friday.

As if this wasn't bad enough, Julie-Ann's blond ringletted

hair, no doubt another of Mrs Jones' creations, bobbed and bounced animatedly upon her soft angora shoulders. Ah yes, Julie-Ann Jones, how I envied you, the girl who had everything. Unknowingly, she taught me a valuable lesson at an early age – life just isn't fair. Looking at the later frumpy version of my childhood heroine as she walked off towards the car park, I wondered how her life had turned out, given the marvellous start she'd had with such an attentive mother!

In the supermarket Mum closely examined the items on the shelves. Picking up tins of mandarins, she studied the prices, taking time to compare them.

'They're cheaper in Tesco's,' she finally announced, indicating that we move on. The next stop was the tins of peas, where she looked at one brand and then another as the seconds turned to minutes.

'They're probably cheaper in Tesco's too,' I suggested hopefully, but that didn't work.

'No, they're two pence dearer there.'

Having spent much of my adult life in a "time famine" caused mainly by the pressure of a busy schedule, it seemed ludicrous standing there in Asda that morning while Mum squandered her last precious bit of life on earth trying to calculate which tin of peas to buy.

'How about we have some nice fresh salmon and salad for lunch today, Mum? Some good healthy omega 3, eh?'

That broke the focus on the peas. Wheeling her to the fish counter, I requested two tails of fresh salmon.

'I'll pay for this, Mum.' I didn't want to stand there again while she studiously compared salmon prices. Looking aghast at the two pink pieces of fish being weighed by the assistant, the side of Mum's upper lip began to move in its usual upward direction.

'Ooh God, *that's* not salmon!' she stated incredulously. 'It's John West yer want, red salmon, in a tin,' she explained. How was I to respond to this new bit of information without causing Mum to feel inadequate?

The assistant smiled, giving me a quick wink as he came to my rescue. It probably wasn't the first time he'd encountered such a response to his wares.

'Yes, love, but this is what salmon looks like before it's squashed into a tin. This is real salmon.' Even though hearing this from a bona fide fishmonger wearing his striped apron and fishmonger's straw hat, she didn't look convinced.

'Come on, Mum, why don't you try it? I can cook it for you in lovely virgin olive oil. You'll love it; you'll never want salmon in a tin again once you've tried this.'

Her crinkled nose continued to express disapproval, but before she could object the man had put the sealed bag of salmon in my basket and I was pushing the wheelchair towards the fruit and vegetable aisles where further healthy produce would no doubt be up for evaluation. Ignorance is not stupidity. In my mother's world, salmon only ever came in a tin and I'm sure there are plenty of people of the same mind. We can only retrieve "facts" from our personally held store of knowledge.

While heading confidently towards the check-out, with real salmon, a bag of salad and a bottle of virgin olive oil, Mum wanted to revisit the aisle where the tins of peas were.

'I haven't got the peas yet,' she declared, her finger pointing to the aisle behind us.

Playing my ace card, I called upon Routine to help me out.

'But we should be getting back now, Mum; don't forget we have to have a cup of tea and a jam tart at 11 o'clock… *and* get to the betting shop to place your bets before then.'

'We've got time,' she said without even looking at her watch. And so it was back to the peas. My back was aching as I stood there watching Mum resume her scrutiny of the peas on that same shelf.

Once more I reminded myself to be patient as I felt the tension rising in my body. Mum didn't have long to live and she was obviously gaining some sense of satisfaction from this activity. But as it went on and on, her interest now extending to tins of beans as well as peas, the attempted cognitive reframing of my own negative thoughts was becoming increasingly difficult.

Sometimes, when at your darkest hour in life, help can arrive from the most unexpected quarters. It was just then that Eileen and Colleen appeared at the end of the aisle. They were doing their own Saturday morning shopping and right away recognised what I was experiencing. They enjoyed a good laugh before coming over to say hello. Taking charge, Eileen demonstrated how best to deal with the situation.

'Come on, Mum, I've seen them a lot cheaper at Tesco's.'

Before Mum could respond, Eileen took the tins from her hands and plonked them back on the shelf. She then grabbed hold of the wheelchair handles, whirled the whole contraption around and headed for the check-out. I felt sorry for Mum, as she would have gained some pleasure from making her own product selections, a small activity providing a sense of independence. The problem was she was incapable of choosing what she wanted in any reasonable timeframe.

Eileen was showing off now, relishing her control of the situation, until we came to the check-out counter. When the operator attempted to make polite conversation with Mum, Eileen answered on her behalf. But the woman just ignored Eileen and continued to address Mum, who enjoyed the small talk about the weather and confided that she was about to try fresh salmon for the first time in her life. As we left the store I directed a smile and a nod of appreciation towards this perceptive and caring woman.

Once out of Asda, we made our way to the Tesco supermarket in the New Strand shopping mall. Eileen became the Stirling Moss of wheelchair drivers as she vigorously pushed Mum along, leaving me and Colleen to saunter on behind. In Tesco's, Eileen put the tins of mandarins and peas into Mum's basket in the same no-nonsense manner. Mum looked subdued, her body slumped in the demeanour of the defeated. Leaning down towards her I whispered, 'Are you all right, Mum?' She just nodded meekly, saying in a low voice something about Eileen 'making a bloody show of me'. As though reading my thoughts when I looked up, Eileen took me aside and with an air of authority she advised, 'You have to be more assertive with her when out shopping, otherwise you'd still be standing there in Asda. That's what poor Maureen did; you get nowhere being all polite and waiting.' Colleen nodded half-heartedly in agreement. But at the Tesco check-out counter, Mum came into her own when she immediately recognised that she'd been given the wrong change. She probably knew the prices of those mandarins and peas better than anybody else in the world.

'You've short-changed me!' she said to the young woman at the counter while holding her hand out to display the discrepancy. Mum had given her a £5 note but the change was £1 less than it should have been. The error was quickly rectified and apologies given.

'Well spotted,' I said to Mum, taking hold of the wheelchair while Eileen and Colleen returned to the car park arranging to meet up with us at Mum's flat.

'These young ones now, you've got to watch them. They all want easy money to pay for their drugs,' Mum announced, saying that reading *The Sun* every day kept her up to date with what was going on in the world. With an air of triumph she directed me towards the local betting shop.

It seemed that, once in the outside world, the clock held a lot less influence over Mum. Nevertheless, by 11am the shopping was done, the bets were placed and we were all back at her flat. Colleen poured tea into a variety of chipped mugs, as the lemon and raspberry jam tarts sat prettily on the plates. Eileen put on a CD of Julio Iglesias singing *Begin the Beguine*, one of Mum's favourite songs, which was probably her way of atoning for the manner in which she'd so brusquely jolted Mum out of her reverie with the peas.

However, another reverie was about to begin. Listening to *Begin the Beguine,* Mum stopped sipping her tea. Her face lit up with pleasure as she recognised her favourite Spanish crooner. Within a moment, Colleen, Eileen and I were up dancing in the lounge, swaying our hips to the sensual rhythm of the music. Eileen sang along with Julio, her right hand cupped below her mouth, holding an imaginary microphone. Mum danced along in her armchair. She was having a great time. We all were. There's nothing quite like the power of music to lift the human spirit, and at that moment it seemed as though the four of us were moving blissfully towards Nirvana. But the magic of the music was suddenly broken by the phone ringing. It was Maureen wanting to know how things were going. She was told that everything was just fine.

Music had always been a major part of our lives. At home when we were children, the radio was left on for most of the time, usually Radio Luxembourg or the Irish Programme, resulting in us knowing many of the old songs, especially the Irish songs. Being half Irish and half Welsh, Mum had a lovely singing voice. She sang almost all the day long at home and it was only when Dad came home from work that she became quiet and inhibited. I don't know why this happened, but she seemed to go into her shell in his company. Maybe it was because he was so much older than her. The unusual relationship between my parents was something I planned to explore while Mum was still alive.

For married women with children in the 1950s, there didn't seem much to aspire to other than being a housewife. The war years had presented new opportunities for many women to engage in a range of jobs that men usually did. However, once peace was established, they were expected to return to the domestic sphere. There was a time in the '50s when it was not that uncommon for bored and depressed middle-aged women to end it all in their kitchens, found dead with their heads in their gas ovens. One of our neighbours died in this sad and bizarre way. If only they could have felt uplifted emotionally by music as Mum had, things might have been different.

In the living room of our house in Canal Street, Mum would often sing animatedly along to the music on the radio. At other times, when she worked in her little back kitchen, she would close the door and enter another musical realm. This was when she'd be transported to the world of operatic arias, complete with all the passion and dramatic gestures of a diva. Standing by the glass door one day, I watched her special performance as she stood by the sink in her floral-patterned pinny and a plastic curler in her fringe. The lyrics involved a variation of la-la-las as she sang the beautiful *Song to the Moon* from Dvorak's opera *Rusalka,* her eyes glazing over and gradually closing with the beauty of the melody. She didn't have a trained operatic voice, but to me as a child she sounded wonderful.

As the song neared its climax, she still held the knife in her hand from peeling potatoes in the kitchen sink, and on the last note of the aria she threw her head back for dramatic effect. I stood staring at her in silence. After a few seconds, she turned her head towards me, surprised to see her mesmerised little audience on the other side of the glass door. Without a word she just returned to peeling the potatoes. Where had she been in her mind? On the stage of La Scala in Milan?

For Mum, peeling spuds in her tiny back kitchen seemed to be associated with operatic arias, but the activity of ironing the family clothes in the front parlour generated Irish ballads. You'd have thought it would have been the other way round! She sang love songs such as *The Rose of Tralee*. Tears would flow for *The Minstrel Boy*, with his wild harp slung behind him, or pleading for Paddy Reilly to come back home. I loved it all. Our home was like a musical theatre. I watched and listened in awe.

When *Begin the Beguine* finished, Eileen put on other songs she knew Mum enjoyed. The finale of this mini-musical feast in Mum's flat was Gerry Marsden singing what has become Liverpool's National Anthem – *You'll Never Walk Alone*. By 11.30am our four mugs of tea were cold and the jam tarts untouched, but it didn't matter. It was all emotionally enriching. This communal connection via music was what I'd been missing in my life in New Zealand. I was now home again amongst my own people, enjoying the music and the special humour.

5

To give Mum credit, she did at least taste the fresh salmon but ordered me to never buy it for her again.

'It was nowhere near as good as the John West!' she declared.

Sometimes in life, it's easier to just go along with how things are rather than try to change them; to follow the advice of the well known Serenity Prayer and to simply *accept the things I cannot change.* I could see that any attempts at presenting Mum with the likes of chicken stuffed with camembert would be a lost cause. Common sense decreed it would be far easier to let her eat what she liked rather than continue with any gourmet experiments, no matter how well intentioned. Nor would I introduce her to real orange juice at this late stage of her life. It wasn't any great inconvenience for me to join her in eating fish fingers and mash, or to sup on countless cups of tea for a few months. In many ways it was as though I'd been transported back in time but within a convoluted and oscillating mother/child relationship.

As the days passed, the subject of Mum's terminal illness remained unspoken. The metaphorical elephant in the room was now looming large and was in need of acknowledgement, so one rainy afternoon just after lunch I began with the sentence I'd rehearsed so many times in my head.

'Mum, I was wondering if you wanted to talk about that latest diagnosis you were given at the hospital about you having bowel cancer... Do you want... Would it help if you talked about it?' Already I was floundering, but she just looked at me blankly while sitting stock still. I was expecting to hear the usual tirade against the medical professionals not knowing their arses from their elbows; after all, they'd got it wrong twice before, so why should she believe that this time they were right? Maybe she didn't want to talk about it. But I wanted to know how she was dealing with it. It wasn't emotionally helpful to bottle things up, so choosing my words carefully I continued, 'Mum, did you know that those doctors at Fazakerley think you've probably only got about six months to live?' Hearing myself saying this and knowing it was directed at my own mother sent a chill through my body.

But she continued sitting there in her chair without moving a muscle. Going over to her, I took her hand, making sure it wasn't the sore one. After a minute of quiet reflection she moved her hand away as she spoke, 'I think they're right this time.' She said it wasn't dying that concerned her but rather the pain and suffering that might accompany it. I tried to comfort her physically with a gentle hug and told her I'd be staying with her throughout and would look after her to the best of my ability; that I would be her advocate and make sure she never suffered any bad pain. She nodded her appreciation as we decided the best thing to do at that moment was to put the kettle on for a cup of tea, regardless of the time on the clock.

* * *

After about three weeks of my settling in with Mum, Maureen paid a visit to see how things were. She told us she now had a job working in a café in the city. As a middle-aged woman, she was still attractive but lacked confidence – a combination likely to appeal to many a man. But having been previously married to a violent bully whom the family referred to as The Brute, she said she was in no hurry to find a new mate.

When I asked Maureen if she'd like a cup of tea, she looked at Mum to gauge the appropriateness of such a question, as according to the clock we were outside of supping time regulations. Since Mum made no fuss about this anomaly, Maureen assumed that she hadn't heard and suggested we'd be better waiting until the proper time – 11 o'clock. But Mum had heard and was short with Maureen for being so picky.

'Put the bloody kettle on now! God knows I haven't got a lot of time left to be waiting around for a cup of tea.'

Oh yes, I'd gained some ground in the short time I'd been there. Although the food remained much the same, the rigidity around times had become more relaxed. Perhaps it was because I'd been bold enough to persist in asking Mum to explain why we shouldn't eat or drink a bit earlier or later and how I couldn't understand the rigidly controlled lifestyle centred around clock-watching. Mum had given a little ground here and there, until a new, more flexible norm began to develop. Raising the subject of cancer and her only having a few months left to live probably played its part in reducing the control of the clock over what we did and when we did it.

Possibly sensing a hint of guilt or fear in Maureen, Mum spoke to her as though she were a traitor for giving up her caring role. I'd seen this sense of entitlement develop in similar situations – the perceived violation of rights when the long-term helper is no longer around to accede to the demands of the helped. Mum even accused Maureen of hiding the cancer diagnosis from her, saying that she'd had a right to know. But she had been told. Eileen had been there when the doctor at Fazakerley Hospital had explained the situation to her. Maureen looked as though she was about to cry, so I thought it useful just then to remind Mum how well her youngest daughter had looked after her over the last three years. But Mum's lack of response or acknowledgement on hearing this only increased Maureen's sense of hurt, creating her bottom lip to quiver uncontrollably.

In the kitchen I gently touched Maureen's shoulder as she tried to hide her distress.

'Why does she always have to be so bloody horrible to *me*?' she whispered. I said I didn't know the answer to that but sometimes people can become uncharacteristically grumpy in their old age.

'But it's not uncharacteristic of her, is it? She's never had a good word to say about me, not ever. You're supposed to be a therapist; you tell me what's going on there!'

On reflection, what Maureen was saying did hold some truth. I was brought up in the same household, but as a teenager you're so caught up in your own world it's easy to miss what's going on right under your nose in the family setting. Mum *was* often annoyed with Maureen but we just assumed our little sister really was a nuisance.

I asked Maureen if she'd like to come and have lunch with us on a regular basis if she could, and when Mum had her afternoon nap we could talk and get to know each other a bit better. As things were, we were like strangers. She said she'd try to fit something in but seemed too preoccupied and agitated to organise a date, no doubt still upset over the way Mum had spoken to her. Sadly, she never did take me up on the offer to develop a closer sisterly relationship.

Maureen didn't stay long that day as she had to catch the train into the city for her afternoon shift. It was good to notice Mum making the effort to look up and say 'Tara' to her before she left, probably feeling a bit mean after being reminded of her youngest daughter's years of dedicated care.

* * *

There was one specifically timed routine that Mum would never want to change and that involved her horse-racing bets. Saturday mornings was when she opened the racing section of *The Sun* to study the horses that would be running in the afternoon races that day. Sitting next to her, I watched as she carefully considered the form of the horses in each race, explaining to me the formula she used for choosing those she'd place bets on. She told me how important it was to look at a horse's racing record and to never choose a horse simply because you liked the sound of its name. I learned all about the odds-on favourites and the outsiders; that the stayers were the best horses for long distance races and sprinters performed best over short distances. Handicaps based on a jockey's weight were also considered in her selections, as a good horse carrying too much weight would be slowed down.

Mum had always enjoyed betting on the horses as far back as I can remember but I'd never taken much notice. While living in the UK, I'd only ever enjoyed an annual flutter on a horse running in the Grand National, chosen specifically because of its name. In New Zealand it was much the same, the once-a-year big race down under being the Melbourne Cup.

To make sure she didn't miss any of the televised races coming up, Mum organised her afternoon nap earlier on Saturdays. Sitting with her during the racing, I was more interested in watching her than the television. As the horses and the commentator's voice gained speed towards the end of each race, her body moved towards the edge of her chair with her clenched little hands holding her chin. More often than not, the horses she'd picked would win or be placed (coming in second or third), and on the Monday morning I'd pop across to the local betting shop in The Strand to pick up her winnings. It was never much, but it seemed to give her a tremendous amount of excitement and satisfaction.

Another routine pleasure for Mum was watching her favourite TV programme, *Coronation Street.* Once this was out of the way and before supper began, the evenings became a time when Mum and I talked about the past. As the special memorial service was coming up soon, where she would be formally recognised as being the last remaining survivor of the Bootle air-raid shelter that was bombed during World War Two, it presented an opportunity for her to talk about her life. She wasted no time in recalling yet again that awful time in Liverpool's history.

In May 1941, for six nights in a row, German bombers flew across the skies of Liverpool, destroying thousands of homes and buildings and killing and injuring thousands of Liverpudlians. That time in history is known as the May Blitz. As the warning sirens wailed, people hurried to their local air-raid shelters. These were underground bunkers where they congregated until the all-clear sirens were heard. Although people might have breathed a sigh of relief as they clambered safely from the bunkers, grateful to be still alive, their homes may not have survived the blasts or, worse still, the people they loved who couldn't make it to the shelters in time might no longer exist.

On the night of 7th May 1941, when my mother was a teenage girl, she and her mother heard the high-pitched sound of sirens warning of approaching German planes and quickly left their little terraced house in Rhyl Street. When they arrived at the shelter, it was full, but as enemy aircraft were already approaching overhead and bombs were beginning to fall, the officer in attendance at the shelter must have felt sorry for the two frightened females because he allowed them to squeeze inside, huddled together on the steps close by the entrance. Mum said there was the sound of babies crying inside the shelter and people trying to cope with what was happening outside by singing hymns or popular songs of that era.

The noise overhead would have been terrifying, as bombs rained down, hour after hour, creating devastation above ground. My mother's older brother John had not returned home from work that night, leaving both his mother and younger sister worried about his safety. Although I hadn't been there, what happened next was permanently imprinted on my mind, as over the years Mum had recalled the terrors of that night to her children. The shelter received a direct hit from a bomb, killing most of those within. Being right by the entrance, my mother and grandmother managed to scramble out alive.

Outside, the familiar urban landscape had disappeared, leaving the surrounding area unrecognisable. Shops, houses, pubs and churches were engulfed in a swirling fire. As my grandmother and Mum tried to orientate themselves, bombs were still falling, making a whizzing sound before exploding as they hit the ground. Gigantic flames along the whole length of Bootle's docks lit up the night sky across the River Mersey like an Armageddon sunset. It was as though Hitler had ordered the Luftwaffe to obliterate the city of Liverpool, especially the Bootle area and surrounding dockland.

My grandmother became so distressed she was unable to cope with the situation, leaving her young daughter to take the lead in trying to navigate their way home through such mayhem. Throughout our childhoods, this is the story we listened to, told with all the shocking detail and fearful emotion as our mother relived it in the telling. From a therapeutic aspect, verbally relating the terrors of that time over and over would have been helpful for Mum, as it can be a way of extinguishing any underlying post-traumatic stress. However, these frightening images were stamped on the psyches of her impressionable little girls, resulting in childhood nightmares of being burned alive or buried under rubble.

Prior to the May Blitz, Liverpool was also heavily bombed for three nights during December 1940. Occurring just a few days before Christmas, it became known as the Christmas Blitz. Almost 15,000 homes in Bootle were destroyed during the blitzes and over 2,000 people killed or injured. It was therefore important to keep alive the memory of what local people had endured during that most horrible of times in Liverpool's history.

Mum looked sad as she finished telling her story of that night. In addition to the horrors of the war, she went on to describe feeling particularly bitter about the extreme poverty she'd endured as a child during the Great Depression of the 1930s. The descriptions she provided of those times were heart-breaking to hear – feelings of hunger a lot of the time, no Sunday dinner, no Christmas dinner and no Christmas presents. She recollected one particularly bleak Christmas Day drawing a face on her knee and cradling it as though it were a new doll. To think that any child in England today would give themselves such a Christmas present. On hearing this I gently put my arm around Mum's shoulders. She didn't object or try to discourage my physical display of sympathy for that poor little girl.

After leaving school at fourteen to work in a nut processing factory for a few years, Mum then went to work in the Richmond sausage works in Litherland, where she stayed until marrying our dad. At the Richmond she was on her feet all day, and when the factory was bombed during the war every window was blown out, leaving the workers to shiver all day as the cold wind blew through the building while they continued their jobs producing sausages for the people of Liverpool.

Despite these hardships, Mum said that working in the Richmond provided some of the happiest years of her life.

'Were you not happier getting married and having your own home and family, Mum?' There was no immediate answer but I was used to people spending time to think before answering such questions.

'I loved dancing, but once I met your dad that all stopped.'

'Why was that?'

'He couldn't dance.' Anticipating my next question about why he couldn't simply learn how to dance, she added, 'He wasn't interested in it.'

Mum went on to explain how she loved ballroom dancing and that the shortage of men during the war hadn't stopped the women from dancing, as they danced with each other. I then asked what I thought would be another obvious question, 'Why couldn't you have continued to go dancing with your female friends when you were married to Dad?'

Wearing an expression of bewilderment, Mum shook her head as though I'd suggested something as outlandish as her dancing about naked in a cemetery at midnight.

'Ooh God, he wouldn't have liked me doing that!'

She went on to tell me about John, a boyfriend she knew shortly after the war ended who was a marvellous dancer.

'He knew all the steps to all the dances.' She paused for a moment as she reflected on that time of her life. 'He was a lot older than me, always well dressed and polite.'

Apparently this charming Silver Fox was highly sought after given the dearth of young men returning home from the war. He also happened to be the Fred Astaire of the local dance halls. I didn't think Mum had spoken of him before as none of my sisters seemed to know anything about him when I mentioned it later.

'He went off with some other woman who was supposed to be me friend,' she added.

After a pause spent staring down at her clasped hands, she continued, 'And then I met your dad and got married.' Our father was an older man too. He'd been married before but it hadn't worked out well and there were no children. What a time it must have been for those women whose boyfriends, fiancés or husbands never returned from the war, and for women like my mum, leaving their jobs and the dance floor to embrace domesticity with older men.

Before our conversation ended, Mum added that she often thought about her lost love, John Thornton, and the way he'd whirled her around the dance floor. The waltzes, the foxtrots and the 'lovely music'. I'd not made much progress with Mum in regard to my culinary aspirations, but with her talking like this I was in my element as a therapist, gently helping her to open up and tell me about her secret life, the part I knew nothing about.

As a new routine was established, the evening talks with Mum became something we both looked forward to. I mostly took the role of listener and she, like many elderly people, enjoyed talking about the past, which was where most of her life now lay. As well as recalling the familiar funny stories from her younger days and the awful times she endured during the war years, Mum was beginning to open up about the more private side of her life. If she had been one of my clients, rather than my mother, I would have kept notes in her file to remind me of what had been said. But I had no need for any of that. I took it all in, contemplating and remembering every detail she told me.

'What was it like for you having children, Mum?' It was a question I'd often asked clients but when as close to home as this it was a hard one for a mother to answer.

'Full of ups and downs,' she replied. A very general statement and a fair enough description that most parents might put forward. I searched for something a bit more specific.

'What sort of things created the ups?' The length of time she was taking to answer this question made me regret asking it and I became increasingly uncomfortable about what she might say.

'I used to like buying you all new frocks every Easter, picking out which colours would suit each of you, and the shoes and socks to go with them. I used to get the bus to TJ Hughes in town while you were all at school. Yeh, I really enjoyed doing that.'

I couldn't believe what I was hearing. For that to be the highlight of her mothering role!

'And I used to like you all coming into the big bed on a Saturday morning when your dad went to work, and we'd all lie there together until about ten. Me, you, Colleen and Eileen, the four of us looking at the pictures of all the things you could buy in the Littlewoods catalogue.'

Well, she'd enjoyed our company then; that was good. Yes, I remember that catalogue, packed with everything we admired but couldn't afford – clothes, furniture, toys, jewellery, home appliances. When I think back, that catalogue was the only "book" in our childhood home!

'That would have been before Maureen was born, wouldn't it?' I asked.

'Oh yeh, things were different once she arrived.'

'In what way?'

'You know your dad died the same year she was born, and bringing up four kids on me own wasn't easy.' It was strange how from my perspective she appeared to blossom and enjoy life once Dad had died.

'It must have been really hard for you, Mum. You were only in your thirties, weren't you? A young age to be widowed.'

I noticed she was now repeatedly looking at the clock, a sure sign she was becoming agitated and perhaps moving into uncharted waters.

'Well, you did an amazing job of it, Mum,' I said in all sincerity. 'When I think back to my childhood and being at home, it was a happy time all right. I didn't like going to school though, but being home was where I felt secure, a place where I could just be me.' It seemed strange to hear myself saying such things, opening up as though I'd now become the client.

'*You* weren't much trouble,' Mum said softly, with such an expression of tenderness I thought she might start weeping. But then she asked for the TV to be turned on, even though we normally didn't watch anything after 9pm. Activities such as switching on a television set or filling a kettle can be used to break the discomfort of an unwanted conversation. Emotional safety nets. We sat there in silence looking at some inane reality TV show.

There seemed to be something lurking there in the past, something Mum didn't want to discuss. I had been there, living within that family, right up to the age of eighteen when I left to get married, but I didn't really have a clue what might have been going on for Mum. Part of me wanted to leave well alone and to stop asking questions. After all, she was dying. Another part of me wanted to take this opportunity, one that would never come again, to find out more about the hidden areas of her life.

After pretending to watch TV for a while, we both decided that the programme was 'just a load of rubbish' and therefore a good enough reason to turn in. We hardly spoke as I helped Mum to bed, giving her a little kiss on the forehead. She let out a long sigh as though she was about to say something, but then changed her mind.

'What is it, Mum? Is there something you want to tell me?' Her mouth opened but then closed again without speaking.

'Is it something about the old days? Something you want to get off your chest?'

Shaking her head she answered, 'No, it's not about the past.' Then she went quiet again.

'What is it, Mum? You can tell me; maybe I can be of some help to you.' I waited while she contemplated what she should do. Finally she told me what the problem was.

'I'm being robbed. All me savings are disappearing, and it's not me getting into it, it's somebody else.'

'Your bank account's being interfered with?'

'No, it's me savings, the money I put away every week. Someone's dipping into it.'

'God, Mum! Are you sure?'

'Yes, I know that for sure. When I count it, it's gone down again.'

'Who the hell would do a thing like that? Rob a pensioner of her savings? How would they get into the flat?'

'I know who it is but I can't say anything 'cos she'll just deny it.'

'Who is it?'

'It's the carer, Laura. It's been going on for a few years now, ever since she came on the scene. It's a terrible thing to have a thief in your own home.'

'Bloody hell, Mum, that's shocking! How do you know it's her?'

'It's her all right. I keep an eye on her and she's always

sneaking off and leaving Brenda with me when we're in the bathroom. I've left a few little traps for her, but she's cunning, bides her time and then makes her move.' Mum's expression was now very intense. The energy of anger was rising in my own body too.

'Have you told the others? You can't be putting up with that sort of thing. It's a criminal act.'

'Maureen knows all about it, but she says we need proof before we can say or do anything and we've never been able to catch her in the act. She always seems to be one step ahead.'

'How much has been taken?'

'Thousands.'

'Oh my God! That's serious. We should get the police involved.'

'She'll just deny it.'

If Laura was a thief, then she would more than likely be doing the same to her other elderly clients and might even have a past record of stealing. After some thought I suggested we could ring the agency that employed Laura and have her records checked for any previous convictions, but Mum shook her head – 'No, Maureen's looked into all that and it came to nothing.' Mum's fists were tightening with the injustice of it all.

'When was the last time you knew for sure that money had been taken?'

'It was down another £500 from when I last counted it, and that was just last week.'

'What a bloody nerve; the woman's a criminal!' My fists were also tensing up. I could hardly believe what I was hearing.

'Where is this money?' She didn't answer, so obviously didn't trust telling me.

'Well, from now on maybe you put what you've got in the bank and don't hide any more cash away. I'll just draw enough out for your weekly groceries, your purse money, and the rest can stay in your bank account. She won't be able to get it there. All your regular bills can be paid by direct debit, so you won't need cash to pay for any of them.' Mum didn't look too happy about my suggestion.

'Do you trust me enough to do that for you? I can set up direct debits so that all your bills, the rent, the power, the phone and gas are all paid automatically out of your bank account instead of me having to go and get your pension money to use cash for everything.'

She nodded compliantly but wanted to keep her stash of money hidden away for emergencies, agreeing that she wouldn't add any more to it. For Mum, money had been an important part of her independence. She'd lost her physical freedom and was now losing all financial autonomy.

'It's not good to have a lot of cash hidden in the house, Mum. I really think it would be safer in the bank. I could put it in your account for you.' But no, Mum was insistent on having her 'rainy day' money at hand, not fully trusting the banks as they could 'go bust' overnight.

And so it was decided that Mum would keep her stash of money but not add any more to it. Meanwhile, I would try to work out a way of gaining some evidence against Laura so we could involve the police.

'Don't worry yourself about it, Mum, you just leave it to me while I think about how to go about catching her in the act.' Bending down, I gave her another gentle little kiss on the forehead.

'Good night and God bless,' I said, turning out the light. 'Night night now.'

6

My poor Mum. Being robbed in her own home. What a distressing situation for her to experience at such an advanced age. In her 92nd year, there were so many good things she'd never experienced. For example, she'd never been in a swimming pool or in the sea, not even dipped a toe in the River Mersey. She'd never tasted the delights of an authentic Indian or Thai meal. She'd never been in an aeroplane. She'd never ventured further than Blackpool to the north of Liverpool or beyond Colwyn Bay to the south. Outside of her routine life in Bootle, there was no curiosity about what other places in the world might be like.

However, during one of our evening talks she did admit to thinking that a cruise might have been nice, as long as she didn't have to get off the ship to see any 'foreign places'. She'd heard that people could go ballroom dancing on those big Cunard cruise liners – the *Queen Elizabeth, Queen Mary 2* and *Queen Victoria* – and for her this seemed to be the main appeal of such a holiday. Dancing around the world without setting a foot ashore! There was also the fact that the Cunard line had early ties with Liverpool, so the Merseyside connection created some appeal for her too. But now in her ever-increasing state of frailty, it was too late. I'd been with her for only a few weeks and already she was becoming noticeably weaker.

When Laura and Brenda arrived the following morning, I took particular note of how they operated. Laura came across as loud and overbearing. Her dyed blond hair was buffed up high on her head and the amount of make-up and glitzy ostentatious jewellery she was wearing seemed incongruous with the job. 'A right scutty' was how Mum described her. By contrast, Brenda was quiet and unassuming. Her long brown hair worn in a plait down her back made her appear somewhat Amish compared to her brassy looking colleague. Rather than keep out of the way as I usually did, my aim was to make conversation. But the bathroom was very small and my presence there would have been inappropriate, so I bided my time waiting in the lounge.

After about twenty minutes Mum came out, having been showered and dressed by the women. Laura was eager to get going to their next client rather than have the tea or coffee I offered.

'Thanks, love, but we're on a tight schedule,' Laura said, putting on her coat and picking up her bag. Brenda also thanked me for the offer, and the pair of them quickly left after a quick 'Tara' and 'We'll see you again tomorrow'.

Mum looked at me, waiting for my response.

'Well, Laura didn't get a chance to rob you today, did she?'

'No, that's 'cos you're here. You usually keep out of the way in yer room, and that's when she slips out saying she's got a call to make and leaves Brenda to dress me. But I don't believe she makes any calls. She's using that as an excuse to take me money.'

'If you told me where the money was, then I could see if Laura goes near it and confront her in the act.' Mum bit her bottom lip, wondering if she should reveal the hiding place to me or not. She decided she wouldn't. Perhaps nobody could now be trusted, not even her own daughter.

'No! If you just stay in the lounge and watch where she goes when she comes out the bathroom, then she won't be able to do it anymore, so prevention's better than cure.'

'But she's robbed you blind, Mum, thousands taken from your life savings. We can't let her get off with that. What did Maureen do to try and catch her?'

'Oh, she did everything, all sorts of things, but this woman's very clever, very cunning.' Mum was happy enough for the thieving to stop rather than worry about Laura's comeuppance for past crimes, but I wasn't. I decided to find out more about Laura, but that would be hard as we didn't even know her surname. A good plan was required.

* * *

On the morning of the May Blitz Memorial Service the weather was windy with a grey overcast sky. Wrapped up in her coat and tartan scarf and with a blanket over her knees,

I pushed Mum in her wheelchair to the end of Marsh Lane and on towards Strand Road where the service was to take place. The mayor was already there, wearing his chain of office and talking to what appeared to be a group of fellow official dignitaries. As a young male photographer from the local newspaper paced up and down waiting, about thirty children, along with members of the public, began to assemble, all providing a noisy congregation of humanity. Eileen, Colleen and Maureen arrived shortly after Mum and me.

In the middle of the area was a large white stone with a bronze plaque in remembrance of all the people who'd lost their lives on the night of 7th May 1941 in the Bootle air-raid shelter. Being the only living survivor of that awful event, Mum soon became the main attraction and was positioned in her wheelchair right next to the memorial stone. She maintained a proprietorial hand on the stone while being interviewed and photographed, the mayor bending down before her as though he was bowing, while shaking her free hand. She seemed to be coping well enough with all the attention and even enjoying it.

The formal part of the service began with the mayor explaining why we were all there. He talked about what had happened at that very place all those years ago and how important it was that we never forget what that generation of Liverpudlians went through. He then made a special mention of Mum, as she sat there like some interesting living relic of the past, all eyes remaining on her as he spoke.

After the mayor's speech, the schoolchildren sang some wartime songs, such as *We'll Meet Again*, and closed with the hymn *Abide with Me.* By this time I was feeling a lump of sadness in my throat and, looking about me, I could see I wasn't the only one being emotionally affected. During the one minute of silence my thoughts focused on the suffering of that awful night – the horror of it all, not just the sufferings of the people, but all the poor animals, imagining how terrified they must have been. Along with their homes, many people lost family members, friends, neighbours, workmates and probably a lot of their pets too. The Liverpool blitzes created a time of suffering that we, of the more fortunate later generations can barely imagine.

What made that moment of silence extraordinarily eerie was the gusts of wind blowing through the microphones, creating a sound like bombs whistling through the air and exploding. It was as though the wartime bombs had returned. I looked at Mum, concerned that such a frightening sound would create some distress for her, but she just sat perfectly still with her head bowed. As I looked at her, I imagined her as that young girl, only fifteen years old, climbing out of the destroyed bunker to be greeted by the shocking sight of Bootle on fire while bombs continued to fall; that frightened teenage girl who was to become my mother.

When the service ended, Mum was besieged by several members of the public and a few schoolchildren as though she were a celebrity. Some touched her shoulder, others shook her hand and most wished her well. As a result of all the attention, she looked the most animated I'd seen her since I'd arrived in Liverpool, talking away in her broad accent, her facial expressions and gesticulations helping to describe the dramatic scenes of that night to anybody interested in hearing more about it.

After the last of the photographs were taken, we were herded into a nearby hall for a morning tea. Mum sat upright in her wheelchair, no doubt feeling a strong sense of importance as people she'd never known continued to acknowledge her, kneeling down by the wheelchair to make sure she had plenty of ham sandwiches and cake. But she soon became tired and her body returned to its usual posture of exhaustion. Pushing Mum back home with my three sisters trailing behind, I realised how protective I'd become of her. I wasn't going to let Eileen show off again, pushing Mum around like a rag doll in a pram. After such a service, a bit more respect was in order.

What a day it had been for Mum, the only person left to tell the story of that fearful night. The sadness of the day was increased by knowing that in a very short time she too would be gone.

* * *

I hadn't made much headway in finding out more about Laura, as she'd gone away on holiday for a few weeks, leaving Brenda with a replacement helper named Barbara. I had, however, managed to contact the home care agency that employed the women and found out Laura's surname, which of all names happened to be Smith. I asked the manager of the agency if all the helpers were checked for criminal records before being hired, and yes they were. Not wanting to create suspicion specifically around Laura, my questioning had hopefully come across as a general enquiry on behalf of Mum.

I'd also rung Maureen to find out more about Laura and what had been attempted to resolve the situation. Maureen told me she had been limited in helping Mum as she'd refused to say where her money was hidden. It seemed that only Laura and Mum knew the location of the stash. Maureen also wondered if Mum was 'losing her marbles', and that she'd noticed her becoming easily confused, especially around details involving calculation, which might explain why she spent so much time comparing prices in the supermarket. Perhaps Laura was being wrongly accused. On the other hand, Mum had noticed right away when she'd been short-changed in Tesco, and for her savings discrepancy to be in the thousands seemed too large a miscalculation.

Later that week Mum checked her money and was pleased to find that it still tallied with her last count. So that was good, although I really wished she would put it in the bank and let me show her how she could check the balance online. But no, that didn't appeal. She liked to see and touch 'real money', pound notes with which she could survive any future hard times – a life lesson gleaned from the years of the Great Depression.

As the Laura situation became less of a focus for Mum, it became apparent from our regular evening talks that music and dancing were what she had loved in life above everything else. She described the Liverpool dance halls of the 1940s (The Grafton and the Rialto) where she'd gone with her friends Maggie, Joan and Irene and later on with John Thornton. She reminisced about the live bands that had played there on Saturday afternoons (the tea dances) and Saturday evenings, and the types of dances people had enjoyed. She also described in detail the dresses and shoes she wore for dancing and the inordinate amount of time she'd spent trying to curl her horse-straight hair into the fashion of that time. I noticed how emotionally up-lifted she became when talking about those by-gone days at the dance halls. I also noticed that since we'd discussed the terminal diagnosis, she'd never once raised the subject with me again.

One evening, when there was a pause in our conversation, I introduced Mum to the concept of meditation. I suggested we try a special little relaxation exercise together to see if it made her feel pleasantly relaxed. She agreed but not before I'd persuaded her that it was nothing to do with sitting upright in the lotus position with her forefingers and thumbs touching like a Buddha and that these physical extras were just the bells and whistles some people found helpful but were not essential to meditating and could even put people off trying it. Mum had never been in favour of people having 'therapy', explaining: 'What we went through during the war, there were no counsellors asking us how we felt, we just had to get on with it, otherwise there'd have been no one left to feel anything!' According to Mum, psychological therapy just made weak people even weaker.

But she agreed to try meditation, so, after making sure she was as comfortable as she could be sitting in her armchair with a cushion to support her head (this in itself was no easy task as it took many attempts to get the cushion just right), together we closed our eyes and I asked her to just focus on her own body breathing in and out; to let her body breathe of its own accord and for her to simply be an observer of her lungs getting on with the repetitive job of taking air in and letting it out to keep her alive.

After a few minutes I asked how that was for her. She slowly opened her eyes and replied that yes she did feel more relaxed. This was better than I'd hoped for, especially after experiencing her negative reaction towards anything new, such as the salmon. I pushed my luck a bit further by introducing another exercise, this time involving imagery, and asked if she would like a coastal or a country scene to conjure up in her imagination. But her lip began to curl, followed by the usual crinkle of negativity around her nose.

'What good would that do?' she asked.

'It's just another way of getting your mind and body to relax. You could just try it and see if it works. Some people find it even more relaxing than the breathing exercise we just did.'

'Is it some sort of New Age thing?'

'A little bit, but let's see if it works for you. You can go anywhere you like in your imagination, you know; there are no boundaries.'

After some consideration she reluctantly agreed to give it a go and chose the country setting. Remembering the words I had read out to thousands of clients over the years, I began speaking slowly and clearly, 'Mum, I want you to just sit back in your chair and close your eyes. Let your body feel supported and comfortable. Empty your mind of everything but my voice. Let all other sounds around you fade away. Just listen to my voice and let yourself begin to relax… Now, I want you to begin to imagine in your mind that you are standing in a meadow filled with wild flowers. The flowers are yellow and purple. The sun is bright and warm, and a cool breeze brushes across your face. The flowers move gently in the wind. You breathe slowly and deeply…' I noticed Mum's feet were starting to move in a fidgety manner. She was obviously becoming agitated, but I persevered, 'The air is fragrant with the sweet smell of the wild flowers. You hear the sound of the birds singing in the trees. As the wind brushes your upturned face…' Mum brusquely interrupted the exercise.

'It's not working,' she said, opening her eyes.

'Why's that, Mum?'

'I couldn't get the pictures in me mind.'

She moved the cushion away from her head and set her gaze upon the solid reality of the clock on the mantelpiece.

With Mum being pragmatic by nature, I guessed that trying to conjure up a relaxing country scene in this way was too hard for her and that the coastal scene might have been more suitable. She'd been brought up in a monochrome environment among streets of terraced houses with no gardens or trees. For her, the countryside was only a vague concept, and expecting her to imagine wild flowers in a meadow moving gently in the breeze could have been a bit much to ask.

Yes, a coastal scene would have been much easier for her. As a family we used to have days out at the Waterloo shore (just north of Bootle), where our parents, whom we still called Mammy and Daddy back then, sat in hired deckchairs on the beach. Dad sat in his suit, his black shoes polished especially for the outing and Brylcreem rubbed through his hair only to be covered by his best cap. Mum was all buttoned up in her coat and scarf while we girls built sandcastles with buckets and spades and paddled in the River Mersey. Our parents sat there for hours reading the Sunday papers – *The People* and the *News of the World* – and pouring themselves cups of tea from a flask to accompany the salmon (tinned, of course) sandwiches.

When I think about it, they might as well have stayed at home. It seemed to be mainly for us, their children, that they put up with the inconvenience of it all. There was certainly no evidence to suggest they were enjoying themselves, tut-tutting every time they had to remove sand from their shoes or when the sea breeze disturbed the pages of the newspapers while they tried to read. But we girls loved going to the beach and we complained noisily when we had to catch the train back to Bootle.

The following evening I was looking forward to helping Mum conjure up a relaxing coastal image in her mind rather than a country scene. However, *Coronation Street* was on twice that night which meant only half an hour of free time for us between the two episodes. This short interval of time caused Mum to worry about missing the second part of *Coronation Street*, so I flagged away any idea of the imagery exercise. Also, Mum now seemed to be suspicious and on edge about what further 'New Age rubbish' I might want her to try next, but she brightened up when I asked her about the music she'd danced to in her younger days.

Two of the songs she mentioned were ones I remembered her singing at home when we were children –

The Old Lamp Lighter and *Love's Old Sweet Song*. As I was looking through the CDs piled on the kitchen bench for either of these songs, I came across a disc of waltzes. Since we only had a short time before *Coronation Street* came on again, I suggested we listen to some waltz music. She chose *Danube Waves* by Ivanovici.

While listening to this track, I noticed Mum closing her eyes. Her body began to move to the music while she sat in her armchair, although less animatedly than she'd been for *Begin the Beguinne*. Nevertheless, this seemed like good physical exercise for somebody so frail, but how the music was impacting on her emotionally was far more obvious. Judging from the expression on her face, this woman was in a state of bliss, and no wonder – the music we were listening to really was beautiful. I recognised the melody. It was a song Mum used to sing about a man and woman dancing together on their wedding night. According to the information on the CD, *Danube Waves* was also known as *The Anniversary Song*.

An idea began percolating in my mind for the following evening when "Corrie" wouldn't be on and we would have a good two hours together. Abandoning the idea of the coastal imagery, I had something far better planned for Mum. As I turned the CD player off and the TV back on, Mum suddenly opened her eyes as though she'd been woken from a dream. I gave her a little hug and assured her that we'd definitely be listening to that lovely music again tomorrow evening.

7

Up to now I'd declined offers from my sisters to give me a short break away from Mum, but decided to accept an invitation to have lunch with Eileen and her new husband James (whom I'd not yet met) while Colleen stayed to look after Mum for the afternoon.

Eileen was eager to show me her new detached house in an upmarket part of Crosby. Along with having a fancier house, she'd recently upgraded husbands, moving from her terraced house with Mike, the down-to-earth mechanic, to la-de-da James who was an architect. Although James had two adult children from a previous marriage, Eileen had never been a mother and emphasised the fact she was childless by choice rather than through any bad luck in the fertility department.

The first noticeable thing about Eileen's new house was how cold it was inside. She said she didn't like to put any heating on, even in winter, that she preferred having all the windows open so she could breathe in the fresh sea air. It didn't surprise me to hear that James's nickname for her was "The Ice Queen".

The second thing I couldn't help but notice upon entering the house was the embarrassing and overly familiar greeting I received from their two Labrador dogs. One went straight for my crotch while the other was obviously more interested in sniffing bottoms. Eileen roared with laughter at the sight of me attempting to walk into the kitchen to meet James while straddling two very attentive dogs. 'You must be James,' I said awkwardly as he was in the process of preparing our lunch.

'Ah, Kathleen, the psychologist. I've heard a lot about you.'

Grappling with two dogs in such an unfortunate manner while being introduced to my new brother-in-law, I didn't bother requesting that he call me Katherine. Given my current predicament, it didn't seem that relevant. Eileen eventually managed to entice the dogs away from me, but not until she'd had a good laugh.

How Eileen had managed to persuade both her husbands to take on most of the cooking and all the ironing was remarkable. She didn't seem to want any domestic identity whatsoever; perhaps with the kitchen being the only warm area of the house, any man wouldn't have minded labouring over a hot stove during the colder weather.

Although she didn't embrace the stereotypical female role at home, Eileen liked to dress in traditional female clothes, usually a dress with black tights and low-heeled court shoes. That day she was wearing a dark blue cotton dress with short sleeves. The cool air didn't seem to bother her as there were no goosebumps on her bare arms, yet I was shivering in my woollen jersey and trousers. Although sisters, it seemed we hadn't inherited the same metabolic systems.

Eileen worked in an administrative role, but once home she spent most of her time playing the piano or walking her two golden Labradors (George and Burt), whom she openly described as being the loves of her life. Her fur children. It's interesting how dog names have changed over the years. In the street where we were brought up, most dogs were named according to their colour or any specific markings they had, for example, Goldie, Brownie or Blackie, or Spot or Patch. Less imaginatively challenged owners chose Lassie, Trixie or Rover, or perhaps they just had dogs with multi-coloured coats so were forced to think outside the square. In those days dogs seemed to be called any old name, not the human names they are given today.

James was tall and thin with bushy grey hair and horn-rimmed glasses. He spoke with an unusual Oxford-cum-Liverpudlian accent. At first I thought he was just trying to "talk posh" to impress, but it seemed genuine enough as he maintained it throughout without falling into either the broad Liverpudlian or the upper class Oxford category. James worked from home which well suited Eileen's lack of domestic interest. In addition to doing all the cooking and ironing, he'd been provided with a daily dog walking schedule for when Eileen was at work. Even the dogs seemed to recognise who was at the bottom of the hierarchical order in that house, and it wasn't them.

Before lunch, Eileen showed me around her home. After being given such an attentive welcome, the dogs now ignored me, lured away by the chicken in the kitchen. There were three reception rooms downstairs – the main lounge, a music room with two pianos and a room known as the drawing room where James did his architectural work.

Eileen ushered me into the music room to show off her new piano. Sitting upright on her velvet upholstered stool, and with exaggerated flair, she opened the shiny black piano lid, placed the musical score on the stand before her and began to play. I was astounded at the brilliance of her musical ability as her fingers and eyes interpreted the intricate pattern of black notes on the pages. It was far too advanced for me to follow as I stood beside her, so she gave a quick nod when she wanted me to turn over the pages. She played the familiar and very beautiful part of *Rhapsody on a Theme of Paganini* by Rachmaninov, followed by Beethoven's *Moonlight Sonata* and Chopin's *Tristesse*.

Tears welled in my eyes. It wasn't only because the music was beautiful, but because here was my younger sister who was raised in a very working class background without any privileges such as piano lessons, yet what she was doing bordered on the miraculous. Such a massive achievement was obviously born of sheer determination and self-discipline. Apart from paying for a few basic lessons as an adult, she was mainly self-taught, so hours and hours of practice had gone into her musical development. The last time I paid a visit she was playing songs from well-known West-End musicals which we all sang along to, Mum included.

'That's absolutely amazing, Eileen! I can't believe what

I've just witnessed. You've really progressed from the Andrew Lloyd-Webber music.'

She nodded her acknowledgement while flicking through a large music book.

'Does James play?' I asked, looking at the other piano in the room.

'Not really. He's had piano lessons since he was little but he's not that good or that interested.'

'Remember our old piano in the parlour?' I asked, knowing that of course she would, 'and that time I got sixpence from Dad for working out how to play *God Save the Queen* using one finger?'

Although I had a good musical ear and after a short practice could play most tunes, I'd never been as good as Eileen. Neither Colleen nor Maureen had been interested in playing the piano, but both enjoyed singing and we all had fairly good voices.

'Yeh, and I got a shilling for the *Skye Boat Song* played on all black keys,' Eileen added.

Our father had obviously tried to motivate us as best he could with sixpences and shillings. If only he were alive to see how his daughter Eileen played now.

We both heartily agreed that life could be hard. That some children get every opportunity laid on for them by their parents, regardless of having little natural talent or interest, while for others it's a full-on slog fuelled by their own determination. And of course bad things can happen to good people; for example, Mum being robbed of her savings. I asked Eileen what she knew about Laura getting into Mum's money and was surprised by her response. She casually dismissed it as being unworthy of investigation, agreeing with Maureen that Mum was going doolally.

'But she's strongly focused on money and how much things cost,' I argued.

'That's intermittent, though. Sometimes she is and sometimes she isn't.'

'But surely she'd recognise if thousands of pounds from her savings had gone missing?'

'She probably miscounted early on in the piece, and just because it's not the same now she thinks she's been robbed. Anyway, she shouldn't be so miserly. She should have a big spend-up or give it to charity. Get some use out of it instead of being such a Scrooge, secretly counting money and doing nothing with it and then accusing others of stealing it. And even if it *is* true about Laura, you know, in some ways she deserves to be robbed carrying on like that.'

It surprised me to hear Eileen say such a thing, to suggest that our poor old mother deserved to be robbed. From Mum's perspective, having money put away for hard times made sense given what she'd been through.

'Lots of old people worry about how they'll cope in their old age, so having a bit of money put by isn't that uncommon. It can make them feel more secure, especially after going through those terrible years of the Depression and the war. I don't think it's fair for you to say that, Eileen.'

'Fair?' Eileen asked while she flicked through the pages of another music book.

'Well, certainly life's not fair, that's for sure, and never has been,' I said, quickly adding; 'fairness itself is a human concept that doesn't exist in the natural world but that doesn't mean we shouldn't keep striving towards creating something better.'

'One day God will judge what's fair and what's not fair and put it right,' Eileen concluded with a voice of authority. She still attended church each Sunday morning and professed to holding a strong Christian faith.

'Maybe you're right, but meanwhile, just in case there's no such entity as God, we humans need to make sure we foster a good and fair society and focus on the welfare of our own planet as best we can.' This was a topic close to my heart but Eileen obviously didn't like the way the conversation was heading so immediately began playing another piece of music. This time she played *I Know Him So Well*, a song we'd sang together as a duet in the past. She knew how to shut me up in regard to topics she didn't want to discuss!

Eventually James rallied us away from the music room into the dining area where a chicken casserole and vegetables awaited. As we sat down at the table the dogs tried their luck with a variety of begging postures combined with desperate attempts at eye contact. The New Zealand Sauvignon Blanc I'd brought was highly approved of by James who seemed to be a bit of a wine connoisseur. For me, a glass of wine was a welcome change from the copious cups of tea at Mum's place.

Eileen didn't drink alcohol at all, saying that it made her feel hot. I began to wonder if her avoidance of anything to do with feeling warm was associated with panic attacks, as she seemed to be using "safety behaviours" around any potentially warming situations.

'Why's it so bad to feel warm?' I asked.

'I don't know, I just hate it.'

Once again she quickly changed the subject, avoiding any further discussion in that direction by reverting back to the topic of our mother.

'How long do you think she'll last, then?'

'She's a lot weaker now. She can hardly get up on her own anymore,' I said, helping myself to another spoonful of the chicken casserole. 'It's hard to say how much time she's got left. Julie seems to be keeping a good eye on her and she's still enjoying her food, so who knows?'

As James topped up my wine glass I was surprised to feel how good it was to be away from Mum, even though I'd only been with her for just over a month.

'Before you came here we tried to get her into a care home, but she'd been reading horror stories about old people having sticky tape put across their mouths to shut them up and cups of tea left to go cold because they were placed out of reach,' Eileen informed me.

'Well it does happen, you know, even in New Zealand.'

'She didn't want to become another horror story in *The Sun*.'

It was surprising that Mum still preferred to read *The Sun* every day, even though this was the newspaper that accused Liverpudlian football supporters of behaving like barbarians during the Hillsborough disaster and then apologised later when the truth came out.

'One of us had to give up our life to look after her,' Eileen continued, 'and it was poor Maureen who drew the short straw.'

'I think Mum's far better off staying in her own home,

having somebody there with her all the time and— ' Eileen cut me off in mid-sentence to remind me why I'd been part of the problem rather than the solution.

'You were in New Zealand, twelve thousand miles away.' Right away the familiar feelings of guilt filled my chest. I took another sip of wine and looked at James for some reassurance but he just smiled and said nothing.

'Well, that's why I'm here now, and I'll stay with her until I'm not needed anymore.'

'I think it'll be a lot longer than first thought,' Eileen surmised. 'We've seen her much worse than she is now and that was over a year ago. That priest from Saint John's was in and out with his prayerbook for weeks. The Hail Marys went on and on, then one day she just sat up in bed and demanded an egg butty.' *Ah, the old egg butty story again!*

Eileen gave her last two pieces of chicken to the dogs before continuing, 'And I don't think Maureen would go back; she couldn't go through all that again.'

I didn't care how long it took. I was there to be with Mum to the end. The wine was making me big-hearted and bold so I climbed eagerly upon my high horse.

'I won't be going anywhere. She looked after me when I was a helpless child, and I'm looking after her now because right now *she* needs help. That's what families are for.'

I downed the rest of the wine in one go before continuing my say, 'Somewhere along the line in modern life, we've lost sight of our purpose, which I believe is to be there for each other.'

Eileen shrugged, collected the empty plates and put

them on the floor for the dogs to lick as I continued with what was beginning to sound like a hypocritical spiel.

'It's too easy to shove old people into rest homes just when they need their families more than ever.' I looked at Eileen and then at James for some acknowledgement, agreement or any opposing view in order to continue the discussion, but nothing was forthcoming.

Although James wasn't saying anything, his facial expression suggested deep philosophical thought. I soon realised, however, that he was just trying to suppress a burp which finally escaped, exploding in a loud belch. To cover any embarrassment on James's part, although he didn't really seem that bothered, and to change the dead-end subject of caring for the elderly, I asked him what he thought of Eileen's piano playing.

'Yes, it's coming along well,' he answered, pouring the last of the wine into his glass. Coming along well? Poor Eileen. It seemed to be a case of "pearls before swine".

As Eileen and I moved into the lounge with our coffees and chocolate cake, the conversation naturally turned to the past as we recalled some of the more memorable stories of our youth. Eileen's first boyfriend was a gangly and awkward nineteen-year-old called Robert Herring who had a car that always seemed to be breaking down. One evening she brought him into the family home in Canal Street and introduced him to Mum. It wasn't long before Mum started telling Robert all about 'women's problems', the breast lumps, the heavy periods, all emphasised with accompanying hand gestures and facial expressions. As he was a quiet and courteous sort of fellow, Mum misinterpreted his polite attention for genuine interest and progressed to telling him about the problems she had with her bowels. It was as though at long last she'd found a soul mate, somebody who was as interested in these things as she was.

'I just went off to bed and left them to it,' Eileen recalled, laughing at the memory. 'I don't know what time he eventually went, but I never saw him again.' In those days it was commonly thought that if a young man ever wondered how his girlfriend would turn out when she was older, he only had to observe her mother to see the future!

With all our laughing about the past putting Eileen in a more relaxed mood, I felt brave enough to ask her if she'd ever had problems with anxiety. She seemed surprised at my directness, but I could tell from the sudden change in her body language what the answer was. Continuing along the same path, I asked her, 'When was the first time you felt out of control because of anxiety symptoms?'

Taking another bite of her cake, she avoided eye contact with me as she stared straight ahead while eating. Finally, after a few minutes of munching in silence, she spoke,

'I don't want to talk about it. Nobody can help.'

'But that's where you're wrong, Eileen. In my job in New Zealand, that's exactly what I've been doing for a long time, helping people to overcome their anxiety problems. If you had a leak in your bathroom and your brother was a plumber, I bet you'd be glad to let him help you. Why suffer when you don't have to?'

When there was no cake left to use as a displacement activity, she began to open up.

'A few years ago I was at the hairdressers and it was really busy there, lots of people getting their hair done. I remember it was a very warm day and I was sitting in a chair in front of the mirror with this heavy plastic cape around me, and Jill the hairdresser was nattering away while she trimmed my hair… That's when it all started.'

She took a sip of coffee and continued, 'It was this terrible feeling of being over-heated. The plastic cape was getting tighter around my neck, making it hard to breathe, and I was just getting hotter and hotter.'

She took another sip of coffee and I could see her hand shaking as she placed the cup back on the saucer. Lighting a cigarette, she took a long slow drag, blowing out the smoke with her head tilted slightly backwards.

'I can see that even talking about it is making you feel anxious, isn't it? Just try to keep talking. Believe me, once you can see anxiety for what it is, it won't be running your life anymore.' As with most of the clients I'd said this to, she looked at me as though I wasn't comprehending the magnitude of her situation.

Returning to her experience at the hairdressers, she described what happened next. 'Jill was cutting my hair, and she was talking away, not noticing what was happening with me, and I was just getting more and more over-heated. Then my heart started racing and I couldn't breathe properly… I thought I was dying.'

She took another long drag on her cigarette. It seemed strange that she should be talking about the fear of not being able to breathe properly, while sucking in smoke.

'So, what happened next?'

'I jumped up out of the chair, pulled the plastic thing

off me and ran outside to try and breathe.' Every time she mentioned breathing she took another full drag on her cigarette as though it was an asthma inhaler.

'Jill and a couple of the other hairdressers came out after me. Someone rang for an ambulance and I ended up in Fazakerley Hospital.'

'That must have been terrifying for you.' I really did feel sympathetic, even though I'd heard variations of this same theme many times.

'I thought I was dying, having a heart attack or a stroke or something… I'd never been so frightened in my life. They kept me in overnight while they did all sorts of tests but said they couldn't find anything wrong with me.' She drank the rest of her coffee and began picking up and eating the remaining individual cake crumbs on her plate.

'Was it reassuring to find out that there wasn't anything physically wrong with you?' I asked.

'No!' she said sharply, shaking her head. 'That was worse. It hasn't stopped. I've never been able to go back to any hairdresser. I have to cut my own hair and wash it with cool water.'

'Well, if it's just anxiety, then the good news is that you can learn how to deal with it, to overcome it and to see it for what it really is.'

'And what's that?' she asked.

'It's just your own body switching into anxiety mode fuelled by a catastrophic interpretation of your own physiology, for example, being warm. There's nothing dangerous about being warm; it might be uncomfortable, but it's not dangerous.'

If I could have had access to a whiteboard and marker just then, I could have made it easier for Eileen to understand.

'I manage it by making sure I don't get hot, because that's when it all starts,' she said, looking at me as though I was missing the basic point by a mile. 'Prevention's better than cure.' This expression was starting to sound like a family mantra.

'But look at what you're going through to do that: can't go to the hairdressers, washing your hair in cold water, not putting any heating on, all the windows open, and I bet there are plenty of other things. All those types of avoiding are called safety behaviours, and the more you avoid the more it confirms to you that it's dangerous to be warm when it's not.'

'But it is, because being hot sets off a panic attack.'

'Eileen, if you want to stop having panic attacks you just need to follow some strategies; you know, things like cognitive re-framing of unhelpful thoughts that fuel the anxiety, learning proper breathing techniques, meditation to calm down your central nervous system, and mindfulness. And graded exposure to that which you fear, which in your case is being warm and your own physical anxiety symptoms.'

Just as I was getting going on the benefits of cognitive behavioural therapy, James walked in with an opened bottle of red wine and two large glasses. Eileen signalled for me not to say anything, so I guessed she hadn't told him about her panic attacks.

'This is a really nice Pinot Noir from Burgundy,' he said,

'and I can tell you, it's very very good.' As he spoke, he was looking at the bottle as though it were a hand-puppet and he was waiting for its response. Then turning to me he asked if I would like to try it. Of course I would. I loved sipping a good wine while engaging in a debate. But instead, I heard myself saying, 'Well, maybe just a drop for a taste, then I better get going. I can't leave Mum for too long.'

James poured two full large glasses of wine which almost finished the bottle, handing one of them to me. He then settled himself down on the couch, swirling the glass while sniffing at the wine.

'I bet you girls have had a lot to talk about.' It seemed funny him describing us as girls at our ages. I wasn't sure whether to feel patronised or complimented.

'Just going over all the stories from the good old days,' Eileen quickly answered while looking at her watch. Turning to me she tilted her head towards the door. 'We'd better get going. I'll give you a lift back.'

After only a few sips of the wine, which really was nice, I said goodbye to James and the dogs and clambered into Eileen's car. She'd only managed to drive around the corner into the next street when she began behaving in a flustered manner.

'I'll have to pull over!' she said, parking the car in a space half way down the street. Turning off the engine, she looked at me with an accusing expression.

'You shouldn't have made me talk about all that stuff; it's brought on an attack.' She had her hand spread out across her chest as though in distress, before fumbling in her bag, looking for her packet of cigarettes.

'Eileen, never mind your ciggies, just sit back in the seat and try to relax,' I said. 'Right now, all you have to concentrate on is breathing deeply, oxygen that is, not smoke. Just do abdominal breathing, take the breath right down to the bottom of your lungs and then breathe out again.'

Along with teaching her diaphragmatic breathing, I asked her to feel the sensation of her own feet on the floor of the car and the sensation of her body against the seat (in therapeutic terms this is called grounding). For her to be aware that 'right now, in this moment' she was 'completely safe'.

After a few minutes, Eileen was feeling more in control, but she didn't want to continue driving me to Mum's place, even though it was only a ten-minute journey.

'I don't want to drive back on my own in case it all starts up again.'

'Eileen, you definitely need a few sessions of cognitive behavioural therapy; you can't carry on like this. There's no need for all this suffering and the limitations it's putting on your life. It's all unnecessary!' She lit a cigarette and stared ahead, smoking. We now had the problem of how to get me back to Mum's place.

'Can you drive back up the road to your house OK?' I asked.

'Yeh, I can do that, but I don't want James knowing anything about this.' And I didn't want James driving me anywhere after all those drinks he'd enjoyed in the last few hours, so I ordered a taxi on my mobile phone. When it arrived, Eileen drove back home in her car, making out to James that she'd just returned from dropping me off.

Before leaving Eileen, I made her promise that we'd talk about her problem again some time soon and that she'd consider having some therapy sessions. I'd worked with panic disorder clients for years and knew that to experience a panic attack was pretty traumatic for that person, and unless they got therapeutic help they could go through the rest of their life avoiding situations that could trigger the dreaded anxiety symptoms. For Eileen, feeling hot was a trigger, which is why she liked cold air blowing through the windows of her home and car. This provided her with some sense of controlling the problem but, of course, we can't control everything in life. She eventually agreed that she would look at getting help, even though from her perspective people who attended counselling ended up brain-washed or brain-dead!

Poor Eileen. And poor James. For a married couple they didn't seem to have much in common. He obviously liked and appreciated good wine but she didn't drink. She was passionate about music but he didn't seem that interested. And there didn't appear to be much honesty or natural affection between them as a couple. All you could say was that they both seemed to be very fond of their dogs!

8

Arriving back at Mum's flat, I was expecting her to be annoyed with me, perhaps even treat me with contempt for leaving her, the same way she'd been with Maureen. But she was the opposite of this. She asked me what James had made for us to eat, clearly aware that Eileen wouldn't have made anything.

'He's a bit posh, isn't he?' Mum said with a look of disapproval which quickly turned into a grin.

'She's already got him running round after her like a poodle,' Colleen added, looking at Mum to make sure she'd heard. The aim was to win a laugh from Mum, which was easily managed as it was just the sort of thing she'd enjoy hearing. Colleen continued, 'She doesn't do any housework; he does everything while she just swans about. You'd wonder how women like Eileen manage to get men like that.'

Colleen's comment wasn't really fair. The long hours Eileen spent at her piano involved hard work, a far cry from swanning about.

'Well, have a look at this and see what you think,' I said, showing them the video of Eileen playing Chopin's *Tristesse* that I'd recorded on my mobile phone. I don't think either of them realised how well Eileen could now play. They both watched without saying a word.

'Amazing, isn't it, that she can play like that?' I said, holding the small screen in front of them. Colleen raised her eyebrows and opened her mouth, looking as though she was about to say something but changed her mind. Mum nodded her agreement that it was amazing, the emphasis being more on the actual piece of music than the fact that it was her daughter playing it. She recognised the music as being the melody of a song called *How Deep is the Night*.

'Ooh, I remember that, a lovely, lovely song, that.'

While I'd been at Eileen's house, Colleen and Mum had been watching the old classic movie *Gone with the Wind* on DVD. Colleen entertained the idea that Mum would fall in love with Clark Gable all over again, but she just nodded off instead. While Mum was sleeping, Colleen said she'd fast-forwarded most of the movie, leaving it on "pause" near the end. It was four hours long and, not being a bit interested in Clark Gable or the American Civil War, Colleen managed to enjoy a relatively free afternoon reading Mum's magazines and newspapers.

That evening, with no *Coronation Street* on to interrupt us, Mum and I had a full two hours for our mother/daughter time. We began with the basic breathing meditation relaxation exercise. Having had an extra long sleep that day, Mum seemed fairly alert, but she still found the meditation relaxing. I then suggested we could try something different, something that might help her to feel really good. She agreed to go along with whatever I thought best. Not bothering with the coastal imagery, I decided we'd go straight to the dance hall.

'Mum, if you could imagine yourself being young again and going dancing, which dance hall would you choose to go to? It can be anywhere in the world: Vienna, Paris, London?'

She answered right away without thinking about it, 'The Grafton, in Liverpool.' This time I had my notebook and pen to help capture all the details for the guided imagery exercise coming up.

'And if you could be any age to go dancing at The Grafton, what age would you choose to be?' I could hear her calculating the years, and in 1948 she would have been 23, the age she chose to be for this exercise.

'What day of the week shall we make it?'

'The Saturday night dance,' she said.

'So, how do you want to look for your night out? What style do you want for your hair?'

'I would've had little plastic curlers in all day under a scarf, so when I went out me hair was wavy down to me shoulders but by the next day it was dead straight again. Everyone had waves and curls then; some lucky women had naturally wavy hair.'

Poor Mum: a lifetime of curlers. When we were little, more than anything else we wanted curly hair. Like our mum, my sisters and I all had dead straight hair. Many sibling squabbles erupted over who'd get to eat the two end crusts of bread from each loaf as we believed that eating crusts created curly hair. But, of course, it didn't.

'Oh Mum, you'd have been better off born in this latest generation where most girls are using hair straighteners to get rid of their natural curls.'

She gave a little chuckle and shook her head, 'I'd never want to be part of today's lot. The people who went through the war years were the best generation of them all. If it hadn't been for us, you'd all be talking in German now, if you were lucky enough to be alive, that is.' I didn't want a debate around which generation was the best, although I did believe that those of us brought up in the sixties (the Baby-Boomers) created some significant societal shifts. However, human nature being what it is, we mostly tend to favour our own particular generation.

'Well, I'm sure you're right, Mum. But let's get back to your night out dancing. What about make-up?'

'Just red lipstick… and some eyebrows. I always had fair eyebrows so had to pencil over them, otherwise yer couldn't see them.' That didn't seem much in the way of make-up compared to what women wore today. Anyway, now for the ballgown.

'And what dress would…'

'Ooh, and me face powder as well!' she added in a stricken voice as though she was about to leave home without her precious powderpuff.

'What dress are you wearing for the dance? It can be anything. You could have a beautiful expensive ballgown full of sequins if you want.' She put a lot more thought into this question before answering.

'I always liked wearing me white cotton frock with red polka dots.' This was good. A very specific choice for the imagination. Anticipating my next question she said, 'And me shoes would be those lovely red shoes I had with ankle straps. They went well with that frock.' Mum seemed to have a good imagination for this topic compared with the country scene the other night. A faraway look in her eyes and a slight smile on her face could be detected as she got ready to go dancing.

'Oh God, I nearly forgot me handbag! That lovely red clutch bag.'

'No, Mum, you wouldn't want to go dancing and find you'd got no hanky. I remember your old handbags from when I was little; they were always full of hankies.' On hearing this she gave a little laugh.

'All that dancing used to make me nose run, so I had to have a good blow between dances. I used to keep me hanky handy in the belt around me waist.' I decided we didn't need to include any nose-blowing imagery for the exercise; it didn't need to be that realistic!

We now had most of the imagery details required to begin the exercise.

'OK, Mum, it's time for you to sit back in your chair now. Try to get your body as comfortable as you can… Now gently close your eyes. Imagine in your mind that you're 23 years old and it's a Saturday night. See an image of yourself at home getting ready to go out to The Grafton'. I spoke slowly with plenty of pauses to allow her time to create the mental images.

'You're wearing your white dress, the one with the red

polka dots. See how lovely you look. Notice how well your red shoes with the ankle straps go with the dress and the red clutch bag you're holding. Your hair is curled, falling nicely around your shoulders, and you're wearing your red lippy and face powder. Your eyebrows are pencilled on and you are happy and smiling… Now, have an image of yourself like that walking into The Grafton dance hall in Liverpool. Can you see that image of yourself, Mum?'

She still had her eyes shut and was smiling. 'Yeh, I can. I look very nice.'

'Now, the next question is, who are you going to dance with? It can be anybody in the world. It can be Clark Gable or even… Julio Iglesias or…'

'It's John,' she said without any hesitation.

'John Thornton?'

'Yeh.'

'How does he look?'

'He's wearing his dark blue suit and shiny black shoes and a white shirt and a blue tie. He's looking at me and smiling. He looks very nice too.'

Mum was really getting into the imagery now. She seemed to be a natural, better than most of the clients I'd worked with over the years.

'Mum, I want you to hold that image in your mind for a moment while I organise the orchestra, then you can start dancing with John.' Walking across to the CD player I pressed "play" for the waltz *Danube Waves* by Ivanovici to start. As the music began to play, I turned the sound down a little so that Mum could hear my voice as I helped her stay with the images being created in her mind.

'Are you and John dancing together now?'

'No, I can't!' she said. Her eyes were closed but her right hand was slightly raised.

'What's wrong, Mum, do you need to stop the exercise?'

'I can't dance with this bag in me hand!' she said with a sense of urgency as the waltz played on without her. Within seconds I'd turned the music off.

'OK, Mum, just keep your eyes closed and stay where you are on the dance floor. Now, just see yourself walking over to your friends Maggie and Irene who are sitting at a table watching the dancing. They're very happy to look after your bag while you dance with John. Can you see yourself doing that?' Mum silently nodded a yes. Thankfully the kerfuffle over the bag hadn't disrupted the thread of the exercise.

'Now, you're back with John on the dance floor, in your lovely white and red dress. He has his arm around your waist ready for the waltz to start.' I pressed the "play" button again and *Danube Waves* began.

Sitting back in my armchair I observed her while the music played.

'Are you waltzing around the dance floor, Mum?' She nodded a yes.

'Well, you just enjoy this wonderful experience,' I said, deciding I wouldn't guide her anymore as she seemed to have all the imagery she needed. As she sat with her hands on the chair's armrests and her slippered feet on the floor, the minute movements in her shoulders, hips and limbs became more noticeable as the music quickened. Her head moved slightly from side to side to the rhythm of the waltz, but it was her facial expression that reflected what was really going on in her imagination. The faint but distinctive smile indicated that a very positive experience was taking place.

While Mum was dancing, I looked at the black and white wedding photograph of my parents on the mantelpiece. My dad seemed to be beaming with pride to have an attractive young woman on his arm. By contrast, Mum looked frightened and aloof. The age difference between them was conspicuous as they looked more like father and daughter than husband and wife. How a moment in history can be captured forever on a piece of paper!

Returning my attention back to Mum and the music, I wondered if she might feel any sense of guilt dancing away there with another man while my dad in the wedding photograph opposite her looked on. For me it seemed especially poignant given that the words of that particular piece of music are associated with a man and woman dancing on their wedding day, which is why it's also known as *The Anniversary Song.*

When the waltz finished, I pressed the "stop" button. Mum now had her eyes open and was blowing her nose with the hanky she'd pulled down from her cardigan sleeve. I gave her a couple of minutes to orientate herself before speaking.

'How was that, Mum?'

'Yeh… lovely.' The smile suddenly disappeared from her face as she looked down at her hands. 'God, it's horrible coming back to *this*, to what I am now. I wouldn't wish this on anybody.' The ravages of old age. I didn't want to leave Mum feeling sad or angry about returning to reality from where she'd just been, and I didn't want to get into any discussion about old age all being part of the deal when we're born, if we're fortunate enough to reach it that is.

'The thing is, Mum, we can go anywhere we want in our imaginations. In real life, our bodies or our situations might not be what we want, but the mind has no limitations. You can go dancing with John every night if you want to. I can put the music on and in your mind you can be back at The Grafton.'

Mum put the hanky back up her sleeve saying, 'Oh, it was lovely to be young again, to have the energy to keep dancing, to keep going with the music. That's what I miss now; I don't have an ounce of energy to do things like I used to.'

'You can be young again any time you want, to move your body to the music, even if it is only in your mind. It's very good for you, both mentally and physically. So, well done, Mum, you did great!' I told her about the results from recent studies indicating that what we imagine in our minds can have a direct impact on our bodies.

She looked tired as she sank back in her chair.

'I think you've done enough dancing for one night. How about a nice cup of Horlicks for supper?'

Without looking at the clock, Mum agreed, even though it was half an hour before our official suppertime routine. How far we'd come in many different ways!

With that first imaginary dancing exercise with Mum, I had exceeded all expectations. Surprisingly, she was proving to be an exceptional "client". However, when thinking back to my childhood and her singing all day at home, here was a woman who probably spent a lot of time in her head anyway. She was a great fantasist when the context suited. I looked forward to taking her dancing again sometime soon, depending of course on the times of upcoming episodes of *Coronation Street.*

The next guided imagery session with Mum was even better than the first. She insisted on wearing the same dancing outfit and chose the same dancing partner for the evening, her Silver Fox – John Thornton. Along with the *Danube Waves* waltz, she danced to a further two different waltzes and a foxtrot, wiping her nose with her hanky between dances while I sorted out the orchestra. In her imagination she really was 'having a ball'!

The following evening Mum admitted to being a little disappointed when we had to have a break from the dancing imagery to watch *Coronation Street.*

'We don't have to watch Corrie, you know, Mum.'

After giving that idea some thought, she decided it would be bordering on sacrilege to miss her favourite TV programme, especially as she prided herself on having never missed one episode in her life and it had been running now for over 50 years!

As well as helping Mum enjoy the mind-dancing, I was still curious about how her roles as a wife and mother had been. With all our talking so far and her enjoyment of the imagery exercises, it was becoming apparent that she much preferred the life she'd had before settling down to domesticity. The 1940s seemed to be the era she enjoyed most, regardless of the war years. Surely it couldn't be because she went dancing then and not in the 1950s? That would seem too frivolous, too shallow. I wanted to know what married life was like for her, even though I suspected it could be more sad than anything else. Perhaps she'd never loved her husband and such a situation couldn't be spoken of or acknowledged in those days as there was nowhere else for a married woman with children to go.

* * *

On the Monday morning that Laura returned from her holiday, I'd prepared a plan of action which involved engaging both Laura and Brenda in conversation. By doing this I hoped to gain some insights into their personalities, rather than have them disappear as soon as they'd finished with Mum. The bait used to do this involved a lavish offering of cakes to go with a cup of tea. The cakes were to be a little thank you gesture for how well they were helping Mum each day. For all I knew at that time, they could have been working as a team, with Brenda being an accomplice, detaining Mum in the bathroom while Laura pillaged her savings.

Keeping within character, Mum complained about how much the cakes had cost me and how that scutty Laura didn't deserve a biscuit let alone a cake. I reminded her why I was doing this, requesting that she just keep a low profile so that something interesting might come of it.

When Laura and Brenda arrived, the cakes were already out on display, presented alluringly on Mum's best plates ready for when they'd finished their tasks in the bathroom. It worked. That morning Mum was given only a "cat's lick" of a wash and quickly dressed. Within just a few minutes she was escorted like a prisoner back into the lounge area where the glorious morning tea awaited. After lowering Mum back into her armchair, the women rallied around the table like hungry vultures.

Following on from some basic chit-chat while we all partook of the morning tea, I asked Laura how her holiday had been.

'Oh, really nice. I'd never been to America before and I'd highly recommend it.'

'Which part did you visit?' I asked.

'I stayed with a cousin in Palm Springs in California. An absolutely fabulous place! I could live there no trouble, no trouble at all. Then we flew to Las Vegas for a few nights; now that really was fantastic!' She went on to describe the 'incredible' themed sights of Las Vegas – 'The Great Pyramid' and 'The Sphinx', 'New York City' and 'all the fabulous casinos' – while munching her way through a second chocolate eclair.

'Well, how will you ever find similar excitement here in Liverpool after that lot? What sort of things do you enjoy, Laura? You know, hobbies and such like?'

'Ooh, I love karaoke and the bingo; they'd be what I enjoy the most. And me job, of course. I love looking after people like your mum.' Mum sat stock still, saying nothing but taking it all in. I offered her another cake in an attempt to soften the intensity of her expression.

I also asked Brenda what sort of things she enjoyed doing outside of work, expecting to hear something about attending church to go with her Amish looking hair. She said she enjoyed Swedish massage and brewing her own beer. How a first impression created by a simple plait can be so wrong!

Once the cakes were all gone and the teapot supped dry, the two women left to visit their next client. So, Laura enjoyed casinos and the bingo. Maybe she had a gambling problem and had been using Mum's savings to feed it. Whether it was coincidental or not, while she'd been away the thieving had stopped, Mum happily declaring that her stash had not been interfered with now for several weeks. She remained insistent that I stayed in the lounge to keep an eye on what was happening while the carers were in the flat. She didn't want any police involved and in some ways I was glad. From an intuitive viewpoint Laura seemed more like a rough diamond than a thief, and possibly Mum really had become confused in her calculations. However, I intended to watch the situation like a hawk and hopefully one day soon Laura would slip up and be caught in the act.

9

I hadn't forgotten about Eileen and her panic attacks. Scouring the Liverpool phone directory and searching on-line, I found a few local therapists who were trained in cognitive behavioural therapy. When I phoned Eileen to give her the contact details of these therapists, she seemed put out.

'Why can't you help me?' she asked.

'Because I'm your sister and it's probably better if you had somebody from outside the family. You're likely to feel less inhibited with somebody else.' But she wasn't having any of that. Finally, I agreed that we could meet, maybe at Mum's place on a Sunday afternoon while Mum was having her nap. These naps were now becoming much longer, sometimes lasting a good two hours or more.

'We can start with some basic education about anxiety and maybe finish with a meditation,' I suggested. 'And don't worry about Mum waking up; she knows all about meditation and would probably be happy to be part of a group session.'

Eileen's long sigh over the phone insinuated she was about to meet up with some overly zealous, born-again New Ager, but she agreed to come along on the following Sunday afternoon anyway. It seemed as though Mum's lounge was fast becoming my new consulting room!

A few weeks after accepting Eileen's invitation to lunch, Colleen invited me to have dinner with her, which I accepted as long as somebody was willing to stay with Mum while I was away. Unlike Eileen, Colleen would be making the dinner herself, although she did mention buying most of her meals as frozen "ready-mades" from the Iceland supermarket. I decided to take a bottle of New Zealand wine along anyway, as Colleen did enjoy a glass of wine now and again.

At Colleen's house, there were cats lurking about all over the place. Two black and white males (Billy and Jethro) hung around in the front garden, while a ginger tom called Bobby and a shy black cat known as Mr Bush resided in the back garden. Colleen was the Liverpudlian Saint Francis of Assisi. Local sparrows and pigeons knew exactly where she sprinkled pieces of cake and bread for them each morning on her way to the local shops, and no doubt even the neighbourhood rats and mice kept a good eye out for her.

Inside Colleen's house another four cats lived a life of luxury along with three dogs. There was a black and white antisocial cat (Whitewhiskers) who lived upstairs, while three tomcats – Jimmy, Mungo and Barney – lived downstairs with the three dogs. Colleen's dogs were Peggy (now known as Miss Piggy), who was an overweight Staffordshire bull terrier strongly resembling a miniature hippopotamus; Rufus (more affectionately known as Lord Rufus); and Winnie.

Rufus was a very old wire-haired terrier with bushy eyebrows and a drooping moustache. With the red-patterned kerchief around his neck, he looked like a doddery old theatre director wearing a cravat. Colleen said he sometimes put his nose in the air and made a 'hof, hof, hof' sound suggestive of a grizzly old aristocrat with alcohol issues, as he slithered off the couch down on to the mound of cushions waiting to catch him on the floor below. These two dogs, Piggy and Rufus, spent much of their time on Colleen's leather couch, lying there stretched out, snoring and farting. It was like a retirement home for dogs. The third dog, Winnie, was a Border Collie-cross. Unlike her canine companions, she was not a couch potato, probably because there was no room for her. Winnie had gained an unwarranted reputation for being hyperactive but she only seemed that way when compared to the other two dogs.

Colleen's husband had died of cancer the previous year and it was Colleen who'd looked after him throughout his long and painful ordeal. Now living on her own, she tried to compensate for her loss by surrounding herself with numerous pets and, for Colleen, these animals had become her family. She fussed and fretted over them all, scolding and then loving them: 'Jimmy! I'm bloody well fed up with you jumping on that table all the time. Get down, you bad lad!' Then a few minutes later, 'Oh, poor Jimmy, are you all right, son?' quickly followed by, 'Ah God, the poor thing's hungry!'

But none of Colleen's animals could ever possibly be

hungry, as she was continually topping up their food bowls with an assortment of delicacies such as sliced turkey or ham, along with tinned pedigree pet food. Their blankets were smoothed, their cushions shaken and plumped up, and each animal was lovingly stroked from head to tail. The consequence of all this pampering and cosseting was spoiled, over-indulged fussy animals. Ironically, some of the cats, such as Jimmy and Barney, had been starving strays, but within a few months of being in Colleen's care they were turning their noses up at roast chicken and looking disapprovingly at a lamb chop, much preferring a nice piece of fresh cod.

Colleen fed the "outside cats" just as well. A couple of them were local cats already coming from good homes, but preferring to hang about Colleen's property rather than their own. Colleen said she didn't want more than four cats living in the house at a time, so when one of her house cats died, an outside cat would be promoted to the prestigious status of "insider". It was a bit like when a Pope dies and the appearance of white smoke from the Vatican chimney signals that a new Pope has been chosen. It was easy to imagine each of the garden cats holding their breath at the sight of the symbolic white smoke from Colleen's chimney, hoping and praying that they had been the one chosen for the new house cat position!

The most over-indulged of all these animals was the Staffy. While at Colleen's house I witnessed this dog, Miss Piggy, lying on the settee and being presented with a plate of freshly cooked hearts on a silver tray.

'She's gone terrible fussy,' Colleen explained while

hand-feeding the dog. Rufus was also hand-fed but was mostly satisfied with ordinary dog tucker. Bowls of food and fresh water were placed on the floors in most rooms 'just in case they get hungry or thirsty'. It was definitely a case of nurturing in overdrive. Colleen had always been kindness personified but not at this extreme level. In addition to caring for animals, she'd found her niche in the part-time job she did three afternoons a week looking after disabled people.

It was important to be careful what you said in the presence of somebody as benevolent and nurturing as Colleen. For example, I mentioned how nice the little Cadbury's fudge bars were that I couldn't buy in New Zealand and how delicious strawberry tarts were. From there on, I was inundated with packets of the fudge bars from Colleen. It was the same with the strawberry tarts. She never brought along just one or two but a boxful of them whenever she came to visit at Mum's place.

Colleen's house felt warm and homely. Obviously having an eye for interior design, her cushions, curtains and carpets were all colour co-ordinated. A step too far, though, were the large bowls of boiled sweets placed in every room, including the bathroom, their assorted coloured wrappers matching the décor of the surroundings.

In the kitchen there was an enormous fridge with two wide doors. For somebody with a sweet tooth, opening the doors and gazing into that fridge would be like arriving at the pearly gates. Almost every type of chocolate bar on the British market was there. Each shelf of the fridge was piled high with chocolates, cakes, trifles, muffins, apple pies, blueberry flans, cream doughnuts, custard tarts and just about every tempting taste treat you could wish to encounter. On the top shelf was a large white cardboard box containing six strawberry tarts.

But, of course, such an abundance of food comes with a downside and, looking at Colleen's pets, all of them except for Winny bordered on obesity. Miss Piggy, though, had well and truly crossed the border and was so obese that the skin on her back was stretched taut trying to contain all that flesh. She looked as though she could burst at any moment. Colleen, however, was not overweight. She wasn't thin like Maureen, but she certainly wasn't as well-upholstered as her pets. Her joy in life seemed to be giving to others.

As Colleen verbalised a stream of consciousness, her pets followed her around the house, the exceptions being the two canine couch potatoes and the upstairs cat who never ventured downstairs because of the dogs. Apparently Whitewhiskers climbed in and out of Colleen's bedroom window as the mood took her, no doubt sitting up on the roof looking down with disdain at all the feline "wannabes" still hanging about outside.

After spending some time admiring each of these animals, Colleen and I sat down to a lasagne she'd bought from Iceland. It was nicer than expected and we both enjoyed a glass of wine with our meal. Colleen said she generally couldn't be bothered cooking for herself – a common habit for people who find themselves living alone after spending a lifetime making meals for the family. However, she was very willing to cook roast hearts in the oven for her dog!

While we were eating, one of the cats jumped up on to the table and meowed loudly before being chased off by Colleen.

'Ahh, God love him. I just heard him say he wants a dozen fresh oysters and a glass of champagne!' I said to Colleen, laughing.

'He's never had oysters,' Colleen said, as though seriously considering the idea.

'He's tried prawns and crab-meat, but he wasn't that fussed.'

'I was only joking, you know, Colleen.' You had to be careful what you said around Colleen, especially anything involving food.

After our lasagne and a couple of glasses of wine, Colleen was eager to serve the dessert. She gave me a choice of four and was happy for me to try them all. I chose the sherry trifle from Marks and Spencer and one of the strawberry tarts from Sayers Bakery. Colleen had a slice of chocolate log. After the last mouthful of strawberry tart, Colleen brought out a large tin containing a variety of chocolate bars, offering me 'a little something' to go with a cup of tea. Although feeling full, I chose a Wispa because I'd never had one before. Just when I thought we'd finally finished eating, a packet of ginger biscuits covered in dark chocolate appeared on the table.

'Try one of these; they're absolutely gorgeous,' Colleen assured me. And so they were. She put a second one on my plate before returning to the kitchen. Somehow I knew I hadn't seen the last of them.

Once the dishes were out of the way, we returned to

the table and finished off the wine. Colleen wasn't used to drinking and it was good to see her begin to relax. She always seemed to be moving about and doing things rather than savouring life by simply "being", even if only for a few minutes. Her first husband had been a bit of a boozer, leaving Colleen to bring up their two young boys on her own. When in her forties, she met Graham and spent some happily married years with him before he succumbed to cancer.

I'd always been closer to Colleen than to my other sisters. Throughout most of our childhood years we slept at opposite ends of the same single bed. In our teenage years, we still slept together but with the luxury of a bigger double bed. When there are only two bedrooms and four children, sharing beds becomes the norm. Some of the families in the surrounding streets where we grew up had ten or more children. How they managed to cope in their two-bedroom houses, I don't know. But for those days in working class Liverpool, to have only two children sharing a double bed was considered absolute luxury.

There were many times when Colleen and I giggled and talked late into the night as we lay in bed together. No matter how quiet we tried to be, even whispering to each other under the blankets, our dad would hear us from the other bedroom and yell at us to be quiet in, his own particular way – 'Will you two bloody bitches shut up!'

Our poor dad; if only I could have understood then, as I do now as an adult, how hard it must have been for him to keep working full time in a physically demanding job on the docks at an age when most men were looking to retire.

Yes, we were then selfish bloody bitches all right. We just didn't realise it.

Raising the subject of Mum's money going missing, I asked Colleen if she had any clues as to what could be going on. She told me there was talk of Mum having some big wins on the horses a few years ago when a couple of 33-1 outsiders came in on a "double" bet, but she never gave anybody a penny of it – 'She just hid it away somewhere doing no good for anybody.' She added that Mum had become 'terrible mean with her money' and that it wasn't right, that she should have shared it with her family. Colleen began drinking her wine in large gulps, probably eager to have the glass washed and dried and put back in the cupboard.

'How do you know all this?' I asked.

'Maureen had to go over to the betting shop to pick up over £1,000 last year for her, and she never offered her any of it. The bookie told Maureen that Mum had a good eye for picking out the winners and it wasn't her first big win, so she must have picked up the other winnings herself before she got too weak to walk.'

'Well, that's good that she managed to win some money. She loves the racing; she seems to know all about the horses. So, good for her.'

'But she's too mean to enjoy it. It didn't stop her looking for the cheapest of everything in the shops and going without while stashing most of her pension money away. You ask Maureen what she's like, she'll tell you. She's gone mean as muck.'

'Does anybody know where she keeps this great hoard

of cash?' I asked, imagining an old sea-chest full of pound notes buried under the floorboards or hidden in a secret wall.

'Nobody knows and she won't tell anybody either, so if she died, none of us would know where this money was. We'd all miss out on it.'

Colleen was unable to keep still any longer. She finished off her wine, getting up to wash the glass and put it away. She then sat back down at the table, keeping an eye on my wine, itching to get that glass cleaned and put away too.

'But somebody knows where the money is because they've been at it, robbing her. She believes it's Laura, but Maureen and Eileen think she's got it all wrong, miscalculating how much is there and then just blaming Laura. What do you think?'

'I think they're right. I think she's just becoming… forgetful.' So, all my sisters believed that Mum was unreliable with counting money. It certainly wasn't my experience of her.

'But she's so canny with money. I can't imagine her not being able to keep good tabs on her own savings.' I could see Colleen becoming agitated, and I wasn't sure if it was the subject of the conversation or the fact that I was so slow finishing off my glass of wine.

'She should be sharing it out, helping her family out, not hoarding it away, being all secretive like that. It's not right. It's not normal.'

There was certainly some truth to what Colleen was saying, but we, her daughters, hadn't been through the starvation years of the Depression, nor the rationing of food during the war. Becoming old and dependent could be frightening for Mum, so having a hidden amount of cash probably provided some sense of financial security in her increasingly insecure world.

'How much do you think she's got there?' I asked.

'Thousands. What with her big wins and all that scrimping, it must be over £20,000.'

'I just wish she'd let me put it in her bank account for her.'

'Ooh God, she'd never let you do that! She's terrified of it going over a certain amount, worried that it could affect her pension.' So, that was what Mum was really worrying about, not the banks going bust.

'It's a shame Maureen didn't tell me all this when I took over looking after Mum. Everything would have made more sense.'

'Maureen's a bit scared of you.'

'Why? I've never done anything to upset her.'

'Cos of your job. She thinks you can read people's thoughts.'

'Just as if!' No wonder Maureen tended to avoid me if she believed that sort of thing. Although I definitely wasn't a mind-reader, I could tell Colleen was really wanting me to finish my glass of wine so she could wash it and put it away. Perhaps there was a bit of OCD there involving order and symmetry that made her seem so hyperactive. I quickly drank the rest of the wine while she hovered over me, finally passing her the empty glass.

Sitting back at the table, I asked her how she was doing now that Graham was gone and what it was like for her being a widow. She said she hated it, especially being on her own at night and that she was frightened a lot of the time.

Unlike Mum, there was no evidence of "Widow's Bloom" here.

'Well, if you have your bedroom window open all the time for that cat, no wonder you're frightened. Anybody could climb in.'

'But poor Whitewhiskers has to be able to get in and out when she wants to.' That was so typical of Colleen, putting a cat's whims before her own well-being.

'And I'm not scared of an intruder. I'd just hit him with me hockey stick,' she said confidently, despite her body becoming tense and fidgety again.

'What is it that frightens you, then?' I asked.

'It's Graham. He hasn't gone.' Her brown eyes were now like those of a scared animal caught in the headlights of an oncoming car. 'He's hanging about in the bedrooms… haunting me.'

'In what way is he haunting you?'

'Voices and an angry flashing blue light.'

She told me that shortly after Graham's funeral she saw a bright blue light flash across the ceiling while she was lying in bed, that there was no traffic outside and no explanation could be found for it. Colleen interpreted this as being a message from Graham expressing his anger at her for feeling a sense of relief when he'd finally died. As he'd been a keen Everton supporter (his blue and white scarf was still hanging in the hallway), Colleen concluded that the mysterious blue light could only be Graham trying to get in touch with her from the Other Side.

Unfortunately, Colleen was one of those people who make the assumption that if anything seems unexplainable, then it must be of a paranormal nature. From a rational point of view, if there really was no external evidence to explain the blue light Colleen saw in her bedroom that night, then she may well have been in that mental state between sleeping and waking when a dream can seem like reality. Alternatively, her emotions would have been in a turmoil caused by the prolonged period of stress and anxiety during her husband's suffering, only to be followed by the grief of him dying. In other words, the blue light may have been created in Colleen's mind, especially if she was feeling some guilt around the sense of relief she was experiencing when that horrendous and emotionally-laden period of her life was finally over. Being fatigued and emotionally strung out, she would have been a good candidate for "transient hallucinations" following a bereavement.

I'd come across such phenomena several times when helping grieving clients. Some had felt a presence of the loved one who had died, or heard voices or footsteps, or even had the sensation of being touched. Such incidents can provide a sense of comfort for the bereaved, an indication that their loss is only temporary and that one day they'll meet their loved one again when their time comes to die.

But in Colleen's case, there was no comfort to be found, only fear, resulting in a dread of going to bed at night. She continued her story, 'After that, I moved into the spare bedroom in the hope I'd be safer there, but that was worse. One night I was lying in bed reading and I distinctly heard a high-pitched voice like an angry parrot saying, "What d'yer think *you're* doin"?' Colleen mimicked the voice she'd heard, which sounded absurdly comical but also terrifying given the context of the event.

'I was petrified. I knew it was coming from the supernatural.' With four cats in the house and another four outside, I reasoned that it had to be one of them; probably the upstairs cat crying because her owner had changed rooms. Given Colleen's high state of fear and apprehension of something menacing going on in her house, her emotional antennae would have picked up and interpreted a cat's crying as a strange form of human dialogue. I put that forward as being my best guess.

Colleen's eyes were welling up with tears, as were my own. What a situation for her; how frightened anybody would feel if they believed such things. I put my arm around her shoulders, which only seemed to make things worse as she started to really sob then. As any good British citizen would do when faced with a difficult situation, I suggested we both have another cup of tea.

After a few sips of tea and lighting up a cigarette, Colleen seemed a bit better.

'Where do you sleep now, Colleen?' I asked.

'Back in the main bedroom. At least Whitewhiskers is with me there, and I'm now taking sleeping tablets every night. Little pink pills I got from the doctor. They just knock me out so I'm not around to see or hear what's going on in the room.'

I was about to ask her how she'd be able to hit an intruder with her hockey stick if she was unconscious but decided to leave that for now.

'Have you had any other weird experiences since Graham died?' I asked.

She told me about a further incident that had also left her frightened.

'You know all those expensive porcelain dolls that I used to collect?' Yes, I did, they were collectors' items: beautiful dolls with long hair and all wearing different coloured outfits.

'They were all sitting on top of the chest of drawers in the main bedroom where they've been for years, and I was lying in bed looking at them, and next minute they started moving and blinking their eyes.' She looked at me to check my reaction. More than anything, I was feeling a huge sense of compassion, which must have been reflected in my expression, as she continued her mysterious tale.

'I put me head under the blankets and waited for the pills to kick in. The next day I gave every single doll to the Hospice shop.'

'Have you wondered if there's a rational explanation for all of this?' I asked, knowing that fatigue and emotional trauma could create visual illusions involving inanimate objects moving.

'What else could it be other than the supernatural?' she asked. 'I wasn't imagining it, you know.'

'I don't think it's helpful for you to jump to the conclusion that it's all about the supernatural. Remember when…'

'But dolls *don't* move on their own, do they?'

'No, they don't, but there can be other explanations for strange occurrences.' I reminded Colleen of the case involving a mysterious smell that turned up every evening in her previous house about ten years ago when I was staying with her. It smelt like fish, and each evening at around 5pm there it was. We could all smell it, so it wasn't a case of one person imagining it. Colleen had concluded that a fishmonger must have once lived in the house and had died at around that time of day and now his or her ghost was needing to pass on a message of some sort.

It had all sounded a bit like the ghostly Molly Malone pushing her barrow of cockles and mussels, from the famous Irish song. I remember Maureen suggesting that Colleen's house be exorcised by a priest so that the fishmonger's ghost could be told to LEAVE NOW IN THE NAME OF GOD. Salt, garlic powder and holy water from Saint John's Church were sprinkled in the doorway of this haunted house, but it took a very practical-minded person, such as a next door neighbour who happened to be an electrician, to work out what the real problem was. It wasn't a Molly Malone-type phantom, it was the humble plastic lampshade hanging from the ceiling in the hall. A broken part of the shade was melting from the heat of the bulb when the light was turned on and this is what created the fishy stink. And as the light was turned on each winter evening at around 5pm, that was when the ghostly 'smell from hell' arrived, wafting down the hallway and up the staircase. Once the lampshade was replaced there was no more smell.

There was another incident involving slices of toast in Mum's flat, which was deemed to be of a supernatural element. Some years ago, Maureen was making toast for herself, Colleen and Mum. The piece of toast she was buttering for Mum had the shape of a mouse across its centre.

They all laughed at it and marvelled at the coincidence of bread being like that, but when the next piece of toast popped out of the toaster with the same mouse image on it and the following one too, they became afraid, believing it was some sort of omen or sign from the supernatural, and perhaps a priest should be called in. But of course, some hungry little mouse had probably climbed into the toaster looking for a feed of crumbs, and upon being electrocuted his effigy became burnt onto each slice of toasted bread!

Colleen, however, was adamant that these bizarre incidents involving the blue light, the parrot voice and the dolls moving were Graham's attempts to make contact with her from wherever he had gone. That these were signs of his anger. She *knew* it for sure.

'If that were the case,' I said, 'then why should he be angry with you just because you experienced some positive feeling such as relief when his suffering came to an end? The relief would have been for both of you. Surely if he loved you he'd be pleased that you felt relief, and maybe these things represent love rather than anger.' If Colleen really wanted to believe that what she had been experiencing was paranormal activity, then it might as well be viewed in a positive rather than a negative light.

'I don't know,' she said shaking her head. Jimmy was curled up on her lap purring away, while her dog Winnie lay settled down by her feet. The other cats loitered about under the table. It was understandable she would want so much life around her as a distraction from what she was going through.

Trying a different angle, I put it to Colleen, 'Imagine if

it was your death and it was Graham who'd spent over a year helping you through all your suffering – would you make an effort from Beyond the Veil to torment and terrify him for feeling relieved? Of course you wouldn't; and neither would Graham want to do that to you. If it really is Graham, then his message for you is probably all about love not anger. Can you believe that?'

She nodded her head slightly. It was certainly a more helpful way of looking at it if she wanted to hold on to a supernatural explanation.

'But it was more than that,' Colleen added.

'What do you mean?'

'After Graham died, I went through all his private papers and came across a photo of him with his arm around his ex-wife… He must have been watching and saw what I did, and I think that's what made him the most angry.' I waited for her to continue.

'I ripped it up into bits and put it in the bin.'

She looked worried again, looking about her as though Graham might be in the room with us.

'It's just human nature,' I assured her. 'A bit of jealousy, yes, but maybe he'd do the same if it were him finding such a picture when you were dead. The other side of the coin would be indifference, but you loved him. So, a bit of jealousy can also be a sign of love.' A period of silence followed.

'Have you told anybody else about what's been happening?' I asked.

'Only Maureen. She said she didn't want to come here until I'd had the house exorcised by a priest.' I couldn't help tut-tutting when I heard this. Poor Colleen left to grieve without much in the way of sisterly support. Why hadn't she let Eileen know, or told me over the phone what she was going through?

'Why didn't you tell Eileen?'

Colleen shook her head. 'You know what she's like; she wouldn't have time for all that sort of thing. She's got a good life, no kids, no housework, no worries. She wouldn't want to know.'

'I don't know about that. Most people have some problems in their lives.' From years of keeping everything about others confidential, it was now second nature for me to never discuss other people's problems, even when it was close to home and related to family members.

Colleen knew of my disbelief of any supernatural claims and that I veered on the side of rationalism. However, in my heart of hearts I was an agnostic, not an atheist. I didn't believe in an afterlife, but neither did I not believe. Given the conceptual enormity of death, it's understandable that we humans desire some sense of continuity with our loved ones after they are gone. At that time, I wasn't sure what to believe, but things were about to change, and by the year's end it would be very different.

What caused me the most concern about Colleen's situation was the fact that she now knocked herself out each night with sleeping pills. I wanted to help her but wasn't sure how to go about it.

'Do you know what I'd do if I were you, Colleen? First of all I'd question whether or not what I was seeing was factual, as it could just be a temporary emotional consequence of extreme grief. With the strange speech you heard, I really suspect that the parrot voice would have been one of your cats, not talking but meowing, and the meowing sound was transferred into human dialogue in your mind.' Colleen was listening but looking down while she stroked Jimmy. I continued on down the 'if I were you' track.

'If I couldn't accept that, and continued to believe it was all definitely of a paranormal nature, then I'd try to see it as Graham communicating his love for me rather than him being angry. So, if you thought more like that, you wouldn't be on guard watching out for things based on fear. Then if anything out of the ordinary happened, such as seeing another blue light, it wouldn't be a threat, you'd interpret it as being symbolic of love, and then you could go off to sleep feeling that love, and be comforted by it because it means you'll see him again when you die. It would be some sort of proof that there really is a continuation of life and love after death. Does that sound reasonable to you?'

'Yeh, if I believed that, I'd be OK.'

'And if I were you, the next thing I'd do would be to cut down and gradually stop taking the sleeping pills because long term they won't do your body any good.' She wasn't too happy about that idea so I suggested that meditation rather than medication might be a better option for helping her get to sleep. Like Mum and Eileen, she was suspicious of trying meditation, believing it was linked to some sort of Eastern religious cult.

But I didn't get time to explain meditation to Colleen as the taxi I'd booked to pick me up at 8pm had arrived. 'I'll be in touch,' I said, putting my coat on. 'I'll teach you how to meditate and you'll feel a lot better for it.'

As I was going out the front door, Colleen asked me to wait while she rushed into the kitchen for a box of strawberry tarts, along with another Wispa bar, two packets of fudge bars, some custard tarts for Mum and the rest of the chocolate ginger biscuits that I'd agreed were delicious. Loaded up with cakes, chocolate bars and biscuits, I climbed into the taxi and opened the window to wave goodbye. As the taxi slowly reversed, the two front garden cats began to meow loudly.

'What d'yer think *you're* doin?' Colleen cried after me in a high-pitched parrot voice.

We both laughed. As the taxi moved out of the driveway, the driver looked back furtively at Colleen through his rear-view mirror and shook his head. There's nothing quite like a bit of humour to help with emotional healing!

10

While getting out of the taxi near Mum's block of flats, I noticed Eileen's car wasn't in the parking area where she normally left it. Concerned that Mum had been left on her own, I quickly caught the lift up to the seventh floor and let myself into her flat with my key. Walking through the hallway towards the lounge I could hear voices and felt relieved that Eileen must still be there.

But it wasn't Eileen sitting in a chair next to Mum chatting away, it was an old woman I'd never seen before. Her and Mum were drinking glasses of advocaat and lemonade (Snowballs) and sharing a packet of salt and vinegar crisps. A walking stick was leaning against the woman's chair.

'Hello,' I said, putting the cake boxes on the kitchen bench and removing my coat, 'you two look as though you're having a lovely time.' They both smiled.

'When did Eileen go?' I asked.

'She's only just gone, about five minutes ago. It's a

wonder yer didn't see her,' Mum said before introducing me to her friend.

'This is me eldest daughter Kathleen.' Mum was adamant I would never be Katherine. 'And this is Milly who lives on the ninth floor,' Mum added. 'It's her birthday today and she didn't want to spend it on her own so she's come to sit here with me.'

'Pleased to meet you, Milly,' I said, bending down to shake her hand, 'and happy birthday.' Milly beamed with pleasure. She was round and plump in a grandmotherly sort of way, quite the opposite of Mum who was thin and boney. Milly looked slightly younger than Mum, maybe in her mid-eighties. She was elderly, whereas Mum seemed ancient. I waited for Milly to mention how old she was today, but she wasn't saying, so I didn't ask.

'Go and get yerself a Snowball and come and sit here with us,' Mum said. 'I won't be wanting another.' Milly must have brought the drinks and crisps with her.

'They're in the fridge,' Mum continued, pointing to the kitchen as though I might not remember where the fridge was. Pouring one of the small bottles of the fizzy drink into a glass, I sat down with Mum and Milly. I hadn't even had a sip when Mum announced, 'Milly fancies going for a dance tonight to celebrate her birthday. I've been telling her all about what we do – the dancing at The Grafton.'

'I'm not that good at a foxtrot, love. I've never really been very good at dancing at all,' Milly explained in a gravelly voice that didn't seem to go with her appearance, 'but I'm willing to learn. I think I can remember the steps to a waltz all right, and I don't mind who I dance with as long as he's taller than me.' It sounded as though Milly was under the impression I was running some sort of dancing academy. I'd only ever practised guided imagery with individuals, so trying to create and facilitate two lots of individual images at the same time would be challenging to say the least.

After raising our glasses in a toast to celebrate Milly's birthday, I proposed another toast to our good health.

'Health is wealth,' Mum declared, followed by the usual wisdom of it not mattering how rich you are; if you don't have your health, then you are poor.

Nodding her head in my direction and with what seemed to be a faint hint of pride, Mum told Milly, 'She's a doctor.' I'd already explained to Mum several times that my title is for a PhD and that I'm a psychologist not a medical doctor. But the finer points of academia were disregarded. It was the same when I completed a Bachelor of Arts degree in English Literature many years ago, Mum expressing surprise saying she didn't know I could paint!

Before I could explain the doctor title to Milly, she was already rolling up her trouser leg to show me her ulcer. 'Have a look at this, love,' she said, as though displaying a Cartier jewel, a glistening ruby as big as the Delong Star. Mum put on her glasses and moved forward in her chair to get a better look, expressing her astonishment with a slight gasp.

'See that red bit there,' Milly continued, pointing to an area of her leg that was no redder than anywhere else. It was time to stop Milly in her tracks.

'Milly, I'm not a medical doctor, I'm a psychologist. I help people to feel better emotionally.' But Milly's leg was now out on show and she wasn't going to be fobbed off that easily.

'It's all right, love, I don't mind what you call yourself, but see that red area there to the left of the ulcer, well that's been spreading over the last few days and it's itchy, itchy as all hell.' She demonstrated the itchiness with a good scratch.

It was hard to look at Milly's grotesque display without feeling a bit sick. However, she'd certainly found an appreciative audience in Mum, who studied the ulcer with the same intense facial expression she wore when choosing which horses to back from the racing column of *The Sun*. Milly seemed to revel in the attention such an ulcer commanded and continued giving us a full detailed account of when it first appeared, how it's colour and size changed over time, as well as the more unsavoury aspects involving its weeping and bleeding.

As with many elderly people, the topic of conversation continued with other health problems including constipation, failing eyesight and assorted operations. Mum must have told Milly about her cancer diagnosis because Milly prattled on about it for a while even though Mum had become unusually quiet. Milly's monologue came to a standstill when she finally noticed that Mum wasn't responding. It was at that moment I realised how emotionally affected Mum really was. To break the awkwardness of the situation I asked, 'Does anybody want a cake? They're from Colleen – custard tarts and strawberry tarts.'

Milly gushed with enthusiasm over the cakes but Mum thought we should wait until we'd finished our Snowballs and then have them with a cup of tea. Milly's ulcerated leg was still uncovered. She had it up resting on the pouffe, a sight not conducive to enjoying custard or strawberry tarts.

'I'm not sure you'll be up to doing any dancing tonight with *that,* Milly,' I said looking at her leg. It took a few seconds for her to get the joke, and then she laughed as she finally rolled down her trouser leg.

But nobody got to go dancing that night, physically or mentally. Mum began to complain of feeling nauseous. 'Oh God!' she cried falling back against her chair. She was looking up at the ceiling like a martyred saint, with her hand spread out across her chest.

'I shouldn't have had that bloody Snowball.' Never mind the Snowball, I thought, what about you studying that ulcer in all its grossness, and even bending over to get a close-up view? But, of course, Mum had cancer and was dying, this being the more likely reason for her feeling ill.

Taking a few cakes with her, Milly hobbled into the corridor outside Mum's flat. Once in the lift, she turned around to face me, announcing, 'I'm 82 today.'

'A good age, Milly, and I hope you enjoy the rest of your birthday.' The doors of the lift closed, taking Milly back up to her flat on level nine.

As I helped Mum to the bathroom and then to bed, each step she took was accompanied by 'Oh God!' and synchronised with her breathing, the words coming out on each exhalation of breath. To see and hear her suffering like that was dreadful. I wondered how she was going to cope with the end-game of her life, as she'd never been a stoic. It reminded me of a time in Canal Street when she was convinced she was about to die. I must have been about nine, and while watching an episode of *Bonanza* on TV with my sisters, Mum interrupted our viewing to make an important announcement. Dressed in her coat and scarf, and with her handbag on her arm, she told us that she'd swallowed a fly and was off to Bootle Hospital. She believed she was close to death, even informing us that her will was written on a piece of paper under the mat by the big bed upstairs. If she didn't return from the hospital, then we were to let our dad know what had happened when he came home from work. Stepping into the street in her black and white checkered coat, her last words to us were 'Oh God!' as she clasped her throat, 'What a way to die!'

I don't remember any of us rushing upstairs to look at her will under the mat, but I do remember our continuing to watch the Cartwrights fight off yet another villain in *Bonanza*, albeit with some sense of concern that by the time the programme ended we could all be motherless and, with it being a Tuesday, who would make our tea that night given that none of us even knew how to fry a sausage! Needless to say, Mum did return, feeling relieved to be informed that the dead fly in her stomach would not harm her. Why she had such a histrionic response to swallowing an insect after going through the terrors of the war years I don't know. It's possible that the trauma of that time helped play a part in creating hypersensitivity and over-reaction to any form of perceived harm. On the other hand, a popular song playing on the radio during that era may have had an undue influence, something about an old woman dying because she swallowed a fly!

* * *

Sometimes people come into your life briefly and you never see them again, but we'd not seen the last of Milly or her leg. She limped back into Mum's flat the following evening determined to have her night out dancing. But before we could engage in any of the dancing imagery, she needed to know how to do the basic breathing meditation exercise so she could feel relaxed enough for the following guided imagery to be effective.

Before starting the meditation, Milly insisted on rolling her trouser-leg up again 'to let the ulcer breathe, love,' while resting it on the pouffe. It seemed the ulcer would be meditating along with us. After a few minutes of meditation, Mum was looking very relaxed. Milly, on the other hand, was like an over-active child who couldn't keep still. She rubbed her nose, blinked her eyes, tapped her toes and leaned forward to scratch her leg, probably eager to get going on that dance floor.

But during the imagery exercise, she was even worse. She mumbled and giggled and even hummed along to the music, and at one point she requested changing her partner in mid-dance. She squealed as the music increased its pace, crying out that she was becoming dizzy from being hurled about too fast and for someone to 'get out of the way'! In short, she had spoiled it for Mum, who had given up on the exercise and was now glowering at Milly as though she were an unwelcome gatecrasher. I thought Mum had a good imagination, but Milly was in a league of her own. She seemed oblivious to the mayhem she was creating on the imaginary plane, as the melodramatic side of her personality took over the dance floor. There was only one solution to this problem – Milly would have to be banned from The Grafton, at least while Mum was there!

When I suddenly stopped the music, Milly opened her eyes, looking about the room as though she'd just woken up. 'Oh, put it back on, love,' she complained, 'I haven't finished the dance.'

'Milly, I think it's best if you did the mind-dancing on your own. I shouldn't have had both of you doing the same activity at the same time; it works best when you're on your own instead of being with others.' As I spoke I was looking over at Mum's surly expression, hoping Milly would understand.

'Oh Lizzie, you don't look very well,' she said to Mum; 'are you feeling sick again?'

But no acknowledgment was forthcoming, only a curled lip. After some cajoling, Milly agreed that from there on she'd try the exercise on her own, especially when I offered to buy her a CD of waltz music the next day.

'You don't have to do that,' Mum said, finally speaking once Milly had left to go back up to her own flat, 'she can buy her own music.'

'They're not expensive, Mum, and it'll stop her coming back here if she has her own CD.'

'Oh God, don't have her in here anymore. I don't want to go through all that again!' I agreed with Mum on this.

'No, someone like Milly's more suited to enjoying herself

on her own, then she can really let her hair down without annoying anybody else.'

Mum eventually lightened up and we even had a laugh together when recalling how Milly had behaved during the dancing exercise, Mum even parodying her antics. As we laughed together, I felt a sense of girlish camaraderie between us, a closeness that was developing nicely.

'Has she got no family?' I called out while filling the kettle for our supper.

'I think she's got a son living in Aigburth, but he hasn't got much time for her.'

Poor Milly, to be old and alone. I was glad that at least she'd spent some of her birthday with us.

No sooner had I poured the tea when there was a knock on the door. It was Milly, back again already.

'This CD you're getting me, love, what do I do with it to get the music playing? I've only got an old television set.'

'Well, I'll have to buy you a CD player to go with it,' I said, lowering my voice and moving us away from the doorway so that Mum couldn't hear. The Milly problem was becoming more expensive by the minute.

'Are you sure, love? You'll have to set it up for me and show me how to use it, you know.'

'I can do that, Milly. I'll go to The Strand in the morning and see what they've got at Argos.'

To show her appreciation Milly suggested I have afternoon tea with her the following day before organising the mind-dancing.

'Yes, that would be very nice, thank you, Milly.'

'And bring Lizzie up with you; she'll enjoy an outing.'

‘Well, we’ll see how she feels,’ I said, ushering her towards the lift.

There was a part of me that welcomed the idea of helping Milly gain some pleasure, even if it was in her own particularly flamboyant way. But at the same time, I didn’t want her spoiling Mum’s musical reveries. As I closed the door, a saying popped into my mind, something about ‘No good deed goes unpunished’!

On the following day, while Julie was with Mum, I popped up to Milly’s flat to share an afternoon tea with her as promised. Milly’s lack of inhibition knew no bounds as, in the middle of having our tea and biscuits, she leaned down by the side of her chair and brought out a yellow plastic bag. From this bag she produced a hand-mirror and a razor. Holding the mirror in one hand and the razor in the other, she casually began shaving her chin, alternating this activity with sipping her tea and eating a malt biscuit as though it were the most natural thing in the world. At least the ulcer wasn’t out on show, which would have really completed the scene. I marvelled at Milly’s spontaneity and lack of concern about what others might think. A truly liberated woman!

Once set up with her new CD player and a couple of suitable discs, Milly was able to organise the music herself without my help. We briefly revisited the process of meditation followed by the imaginary dancing details according to Milly’s particular preferences. Going back down in the lift to Mum’s flat, I couldn’t help feeling a little uneasy about Milly. With her lack of inhibition combined with an over-the-top imagination, who knows where she could end up in her mind!

11

During the evenings I continued in my attempt to raise the subject of marriage and motherhood with Mum. As we strolled down memory lane together, I was less direct with my questioning, making sure we spent plenty of time meandering off in all directions.

'Remember when we got our first television set, Mum?' I was on fairly safe ground here as we all enjoyed watching TV, including Dad.

'What was the name of that programme you loved, something about a one-armed man?' I asked this already knowing the answer so as to encourage conversation about the past.

'Oh, that was *The Fugitive*, Dr Richard Kimble. David Janssen was the actor. Ooh yeh, I loved that. It was on every Friday night, and there was that other one set in New York... *The Naked City*. There's nothing on now anywhere near as good as they were.'

It was due to the influence of TV that our mammy and

daddy morphed into the more mainstream terms – Mum and Dad.

'Mum, do you remember when there was a ballet performance on the telly, and what I shouted up to the others?' She laughed as she recalled that incident. Mum and I were watching the ballet in the living room and when a couple of male dancers appeared, pirouetting about the stage in their tights, I raced to the foot of the staircase calling up to Eileen and Colleen, 'Quick! Lumps, lumps! Get down here quick!' Within seconds, a stampede of bus-horses thundered down the stairs. As we had no brothers, the male body was something of a mystery to us, and to see those ballet dancers cavorting about with such audacity while wearing only a pair of tights and what looked like medieval codpieces covering their private parts, well, it really was a novelty to behold!

'Lumps, lumps!' Mum echoed for comic effect as she roared laughing at the memory. It was good to see her body shaking and her eyes watering as she threw her head back with laughter. It's now well accepted that a hearty laugh can be very good for the human body, enhancing the immune system, stimulating circulation and aiding muscle relaxation.

'What particular ballet performance was that?' I asked. 'It wasn't Swan Lake, was it?'

'I don't know,' Mum replied, still smiling. It obviously didn't matter what ballet it was.

'We girls didn't have a clue about men in those days, did we?' Mum agreed that no, we didn't, which is probably why she set herself up as an authority on men in order to protect her teenage daughters when boyfriends began appearing on the scene. Her advice was clear, simple and straightforward. It came with a categorical list of which types of men we needed to avoid. For example, we were to steer clear of Irishmen because they hit their wives and liked their drink too much. Scottish men tended to be so mean that the marital bed they provided was only ever a single rather than a double, and bald men along with Welshmen were sex mad! It only left Englishmen with a good head of hair as potential husbands.

Mum presented her advice as though it were factual, the results of some established scientific study on husbandly behaviour in the British Isles. But these "findings" were only based on hear-say and her own observations of how other women had fared in the romantic and domestic spheres. Although cantankerous at times, one of the things I loved about Mum was the humour she could create via her black and white view of almost everything. And for much of the time, when she saw how these views created such laughter for her daughters, rather than becoming offended she'd laugh along with us when the absurdity of what she was saying was pointed out to her.

With her own husband having been English with a good head of hair, I wanted to find out how she had experienced being married. 'Was our dad a good husband to you?'

Without any hesitation or pondering upon the question, she answered, 'Yeh, he was a good provider. A good father.' I suppose compared to her own father (who happened to be Irish), our dad wasn't too bad. But I wanted to know why she was so inhibited in his presence.

This woman who enjoyed singing to herself all day at home went as quiet as a cloistered nun when her husband came home from work. When I asked why this was, she simply replied that she didn't know, and that she was shy of him, from the day they married right up to the day he died. Being a therapist, I wondered if it was something to do with her own early background. Perhaps seeing her own mother beaten in front of the children by her father taught her from an early age that it was wise to keep a low profile when it came to husbands.

'How did you first meet him?' That seemed a harmless enough question to keep the ball rolling in the right direction.

'In the pub on Merton Road. I was with a friend when he came over and asked if he could sit with us. He bought us a couple of drinks.'

'And was it love at first sight for you?' She gave a little laugh and shook her head.

'No, but it was for him. He thought I was a bobby-dazzler. He'd just come back from sea and… I think he was lonely. He'd only been out with me a couple of times when he proposed. Then just before he went back on the ship, we got married in a registry office.'

Before working as a docker, our father had been in the Merchant Navy, travelling all over the world. Ironically, he said that of all the countries he'd sailed to, New Zealand was the best of all. A country where he would have liked to have settled.

'So, you got married hardly knowing each other?' Mum pursed her lips and fumbled with her hanky, a sign I was trespassing into her private world, but this time I decided to keep going.

'Was he what you'd call a *loving* husband?' She looked at her wedding photograph on the mantelpiece and then back at me.

'Why are yer asking these sorts of questions?'

'Because once you're gone, Mum, I'll never have another chance to find out anything about my parents. You know, I'm interested in you and Dad, and what life was like for you before and after you had a family.' She seemed to accept what I said but by then had forgotten my question, which I repeated.

'Was Dad a loving husband to you?'

'He wasn't too bad,' she answered, 'but I hated being left on me own when he went off to sea when you lot were all little. I remember pushing the pram up Coffee House Bridge in winter with the three of you in it and ice all over the road. God, what a struggle that was!' She closed her eyes for a few seconds and sighed as though reliving that time in her life. She had three children all under the age of four and there were no state pre-schools or nurseries in those days. So, for a woman who had loved going out to work and had a passion for dancing, to find herself on her own with three young children, married life and motherhood must have been like a prison sentence.

When Mum went shopping accompanied by her three little daughters, she'd often stop to talk to other women also out shopping with their own broods of children. When they asked Mum how she was doing, she would sometimes give a reply that I never understood. She'd say she was 'Still struggling along between the immensities'; so I now asked Mum what she had meant by that phrase.

'The two immensities are being born and dying, and the bit in between is being alive, living… In them days life was a daily struggle. I've heard other people say we're all "stumbling along between the mysteries"… The whole thing's a mystery all right.' At last we were beginning to delve into the deeper philosophical aspects of life, moving a long way now from catalogues and foxtrots.

I agreed that yes, life certainly is a mystery. 'We come into the world from nowhere and go back to nowhere when we die. Do *you* think there's any life after death?' I was curious to know what Mum thought about this, as she was brought up a Catholic but there was never much evidence of her being a proper practising Catholic other than having four unplanned babies.

'I don't know,' she answered. 'Nobody's ever been back to say.' So, Mum was a bit like me, something of an agnostic. All we know is that we don't know.

'Are you scared of dying, Mum?'

She cleared her throat before answering. 'No,' she said, looking at a ring on her finger and turning it around as though she'd not noticed it before.

'Well, the way I see it, Mum, if there is a God or an intelligent force on a higher plane than us, then I hope that love, kindness and compassion are part of what he, she or it is about. But I don't know, either. I don't know whether there's anything beyond our physical mortality or not. Some people are convinced that there is and others are convinced that there's nothing, but I don't think anybody can say for certain.'

'I don't really care about all that,' Mum said. 'I just don't want to go through any more suffering than what I'm already going through.' I didn't want her to suffer either, but if she really was dying of cancer then there could be far worse yet to come. With Mum, as with many people, it's not the dying that frightens them, it's the suffering that might accompany it.

I could see she was becoming tired, so it was a good time to have our supper and turn in. As I was about to get up, she said, 'I feel like I've had enough now… I'm 91 and everyone I knew from my generation are all gone, and I'm still here, still struggling.'

'You're a stayer, Mum. You've maintained the stamina to run the long-distance race. That's why you're still here. Some people are like sprinters having short fast lives, but you're a stayer; you just keep going.'

She seemed to appreciate the horse-racing analogy, replying, 'I've gone well past the post now and am all ready for the knacker's yard.'

She really was tired of life, but I wasn't ready for her to disappear just yet. There was still so much I wanted to know about the past, about my father, a man I never really knew. And as to what had been going on between Mum and Maureen, I didn't have a clue.

* * *

Remaining in the lounge when Laura and Brenda arrived each morning, I was yet to observe any suspicious behaviour from either of them. Since the thank you gesture with the cakes, they'd become more chatty with me, allowing me to raise some further questions. I'd found out that Laura had been looking after Mum for just over three years and before this she'd worked in a shoe shop. Brenda had been a carer for seven years and before that had worked in an office. Mum had been her client for just under two years.

'There was an article in yesterday's paper about professional carers not getting paid much for the tremendous work they do. Is that right; you're poorly paid for this type of work?' I asked.

'Oh, we don't do it for the money, love, we do it cos we know we're doing something worthwhile and valuable for the old people,' Laura answered. 'Some of them never see their family from one year to the next, so they really appreciate us coming round to help them. You know, when you go to bed exhausted after a day's bloody hard work, you feel good because you know you've made a difference in those people's lives.'

Brenda agreed with her colleague – 'Yeh, as well as them feeling better cos they had a shower and got dressed in clean clothes, they love seeing us. And yeh, of course we should get paid more than we do, but that's the caring industry for you.' Mum must have been one of their few clients who didn't enjoy seeing them.

'Oh well, maybe you'll win on the lotto, bingo or the pokies one day and won't have to work so hard.' I suggested this in the hope of finding out more about any gambling habits.

'Ooh that'd be nice,' replied Laura. 'I had a small win at

the casino when I was on holiday but missed out on any big ones. So it's back to the local bingo hall after the bright lights of Vegas.' Brenda admitted buying the odd lotto ticket but said she didn't hold her breath about any big wins coming her way.

When the women left I asked Mum if she still believed it was Laura who had been stealing her money. She said she did and that if it wasn't for me watching out for her each day, there would have been more taken. Since she'd stopped adding new money to the hidden stash, the amount had remained the same now for weeks, even with Laura back from her holiday.

However, a new stash was beginning to build up in her purse. Given Mum's thriftiness and reluctance to buy anything that she didn't need, her plastic red purse was bulging with unspent money.

'I don't think we should draw out any more purse money, Mum. Look at it; you can hardly close it shut.' But she didn't like the idea of leaving her pension money to mount up in her bank account, and I didn't want her adding it to her hidden savings, so what could be done?

'How about you have a proper big spend up, Mum? Buy some nice things for yourself, maybe something extravagant just because you can.'

'That'd be just wasting money when I've got everything I want. No, I've got another purse you can use. There's a bigger one in the bottom drawer by the cooker, a blue one. Use that instead.'

The big blue purse was found and all the red purse money was transferred into it. No doubt, before long, that too would be bulging. But it was Mum's money and up to her what she wanted to do with it.

* * *

Eileen and Colleen were now dropping in on Sunday afternoons at Mum's flat for their "therapy sessions", which usually included a meditation exercise. Mum spent her afternoon naps in bed, so by the time she woke up Colleen and Eileen were sitting in her lounge feeling very relaxed. They didn't want Mum to know about their sessions, even though it would have been nice to include her as she was now a seasoned meditator.

Initially, the meditation exercises with my sisters were continually interrupted by their nervous giggling, but once the sense of awkwardness subsided their feelings of relaxation increased. We covered the importance of diaphragmatic breathing for helping with feelings of anxiety and looked at mindfulness as a technique for staying in the present moment of life. For the imagery, Colleen was able to see herself getting into her bed feeling calm and relaxed, noticing the crispness of the sheets against her skin and the softness of the pillow under her head. She saw herself closing her eyes and gently falling asleep without any medication.

For Eileen, the imagery was all about feeling relaxed around heat. Seeing herself enjoying the sensation of warm water on her hair at the hairdressers. To feel warm sunshine on her body. To welcome warmth rather than see it as something dangerous, something to be avoided. Along with imagery, both Colleen and Eileen needed to practise graded exposure in real life by facing the situations they were avoiding. For Colleen that meant going to bed at night without the aid of sleeping tablets. For Eileen, going to the hairdressers, and being able to experience physical anxiety symptoms without becoming frightened of them.

Eventually, with daily practice of these strategies, their anxiety levels began to decrease. As a consequence, my sisters began to view cognitive behavioural therapy in a new light, experiencing it as something of value rather than 'a load of shite for the weak-minded'. Interestingly, I'd been reading a research paper, the findings of which suggested the possibility that traumatic events experienced by our ancestors might be retained in our genetic make-up. In other words, for people with a predisposition to anxiety, it's possible that a parent, grandparent or great-grandparent's traumatic experiences may have been transmitted through their genes to subsequent generations. Could it be that the terrors experienced by Mum during the Liverpool blitzes had been genetically passed on to us? Alternatively, perhaps our mother's frequent recalling of those terrible times became absorbed into the psyches of her children, leading to anxiety problems later on in life.

My other sister Maureen was no stranger to anxiety either. It seemed that her way of coping with fearful situations was to acquiesce and to keep a low profile. Like our grandmother, Maureen was hit by her husband and simply tolerated such treatment until he left her for another woman. She'd known a lot of hurt and rejection throughout her life, which had impacted on her self-esteem. No doubt she too would likely benefit from a few sessions of therapy.

Mum was still continuing with the meditation and dancing imagery in the evenings when "Corrie" wasn't on. She was certainly a creature of habit as during her imagery exercise she never once wanted to change her dress, shoes, bag, hairstyle or dancing partner! She seemed to find solace in that particular scene at The Grafton with John Thornton, who I was beginning to suspect had been the love of her life.

Like Eileen and Colleen, Mum had changed her negative view of what therapy could offer ever since engaging in meditation and imagery. As she was unlikely to be around to see her 92nd birthday, I suggested we have a special Sunday dinner and invite Maureen, Colleen and Eileen. It could be like an extra Mother's Day or early birthday celebration. Just Mum and her four daughters all together again. She agreed, but didn't want to call it a birthday celebration. Already feeling like Methuselah, she said she'd had enough birthdays and the thought of still being here for yet another one was too much. Naming it a special Mother's Day celebration would do.

When I asked her what she'd like for a present, she said she had everything she wanted, so 'don't waste yer money'.

'I bought meself this ring,' she said, touching the ring she wore on the same finger as her wedding ring; 'it's the engagement ring I always wanted.' The ring, which hung loosely on her boney finger, was made up of a cluster of small white diamonds around a blue sapphire. I'd commented on it a while back but she hadn't told me it was an engagement ring she'd bought for herself.

'When did you buy that, Mum?'

'A few years ago from the second-hand shop. I'd always

wanted a nice engagement ring. Your dad should have bought me one, but I ended up having to buy this meself.' She was looking at her ring as though some basic rights had been violated. I suppose becoming engaged to yourself in your late eighties lacked the associated element of romance.

'Why didn't you ask Dad to buy you a ring while he was alive?' She looked up at me as though I'd suggested something preposterous.

'It wasn't like that then; we didn't *ask* for things. He was expected to think of doing it himself.' Poor Mum, passively waiting without giving so much as a hint to her husband of what it was she wanted. However, once married with children, trying to find money for an engagement ring wouldn't have been easy for him to do.

'Mum, if you could have any wish, what would it be?'

'D'you mean for now?'

'Yes, something that you'd really like now.'

She thought a while before answering, 'A peaceful death with no suffering.'

'What about the past? What would you wish for if you could change anything in the past?' This question was a bit harder and I hoped it might provide something interesting about her life. After a couple of minutes she gave her answer.

'Two things... I always wanted a little garden, just a bit of grass so that I could sit outside in the sunshine. I could have had that because when they knocked the houses down in Canal Street, we had the choice of going into these flats or getting a house in Kirkby with a back garden. But I chose to stay in Bootle because that's where I'd lived all me life. Yer can't change what's gone.'

We had a tiny back yard in Canal Street with an outside toilet, as did most of the terraced houses in Bootle at that time. It was only when our dad took us to visit Albert our grandfather in a nursing home in Birkdale that we saw how other people could live. The nursing home was in Birkdale Road, a thirty minute train ride from Bootle. As we walked along that road we passed big houses with front gardens full of roses. These were obviously owned by those generally known as "posh people". I never knew such houses existed and remember feeling stunned by the visual beauty and the overpowering fragrance of the flowers. Yes, a garden would have been lovely for us all.

'And what was the other wish you had?'

'To have had a son… for him,' she said, nodding in the direction of her wedding photograph on the mantelpiece.

'Him? Do you mean our dad?'

'Yeh… If only Maureen could've been a boy.' I sat in silence, surprised by what I was hearing. Mum continued, 'I let him down. Four girls and all he ever wanted was a boy.'

I remained quiet, hoping that she would continue.

'You know what he said to me on the day we got married?' She looked up at me to make sure I was listening. 'He said, "you look like a woman who'd have sons." Huh! He got that wrong, didn't he?'

Obviously my dad was not well informed about male and female reproductive systems. It sounded like something from medieval times rather than the twentieth century. I shook my head in disbelief as Mum proceeded with her sorry tale.

'When I went into labour with Maureen, he rang up

the hospital to find out how I was doing and he was told by one of the nurses that I'd had a boy. They got me mixed up with some other woman there... He must have been over the moon with happiness because when he came to see me that night he was carrying a big bunch of flowers. He'd never bought me flowers before and I didn't know that he'd been told he'd had a boy.'

'Had Maureen been born when he came in with the flowers?' I asked.

'Yeh, she was lying in me arms, only a few hours old, when he came in beaming with pride. Yer should have seen the look on his face when I told him the baby was another girl... He didn't speak for a long time.' Mum was staring straight ahead as though reliving the shame of it all. I decided it was time for her to know a few facts about human reproduction.

'Did Dad not know that it's the male sperm that determines the sex of a baby, not the mother's egg? It was *his* sperm that was creating baby girls.'

'I think the disappointment of it all killed him; he didn't even see the year out.' Mum was apparently not taking much notice of what I'd just said as she continued, 'They shouldn't have told him it was a boy, of all the people they could have said that to. I didn't even take the flowers home with me; I left them in the hospital.'

Sitting there listening to Mum, it was hard not to feel some sense of injustice rising. A sense of anger towards Dad.

'But Maureen was a lovely healthy little baby; boy or girl, any baby's precious. Dad should have been over the moon because he'd fathered a beautiful little baby, and at his age too. He should have been grateful, not carrying on like that. And he died from cancer because he was a heavy smoker, not because Maureen wasn't a boy!' I could hear my voice becoming shrill, but I was saying something Mum needed to hear.

'It sounds as though you were married to Henry the Eighth, obsessed with having a son and chopping off his wives' heads if they didn't give him one.' She gave a little smile on hearing this, so I carried on in the same vein.

'Henry the Eighth would have had your head off quick as a flash if you were married to him. No mucking about, he'd have had that axe sharpened all ready to fall if it was ANOTHER BLOODY GIRL!' That worked a treat. Mum was starting to laugh at the absurdity of it all.

'Mum, just think, if you'd had boys, you'd have been shoved into a rest home by now. Remember the saying – 'A son's a son 'til he takes a wife, but a daughter's a daughter all of her life'... You were lucky having girls.' On hearing myself say this, I was glad none of my sisters were there to point out the fact that I'd been in New Zealand for a large part of my mother's life. But in the way Mum looked at me, I could tell she was having similar thoughts.

'Colleen, Maureen and Eileen have been marvellous, looking after you the way they have, making sure you enjoy music and providing plenty of laughs, and cakes. There's no son would have done that.' Mum agreed with a nod of her head.

How Mum had blamed herself all those years for disappointing her husband, and poor Maureen bearing the brunt of Mum's sense of failure. The irony of it all is that Mum enjoyed having girls. With us she could just be herself, singing and laughing and breaking into spontaneous little dances whenever she felt like it. I'm sure Dad would have preferred her to be more natural in his company rather than creeping about like a servant the moment he came home. But that was Mum's choice and, from what I'd just heard, Dad hadn't really provided a suitable climate for her to flourish as his wife.

'So, it's *never* been your fault for having girls, Mum.'

'No,' she said, with some level of certainty.

'Nor has it been Maureen's fault for being a girl.'

'Of course not. She was a pretty little baby' Mum whispered, wiping away a tear and blowing her nose.

Every Christmas when we were children, in our Santa bags we'd find toys that would be more suitable for boys, for example, toy soldiers, books about war, toy guns, boats, tanks and a fire engine. Perhaps Dad was so ashamed of having only daughters that he told his workmates on the docks that he was the father of boys, and buying those types of toys during his lunch breaks gave credibility to his fabrications. We'll never know. Thanks to our mum, though, in our Santa bags there were also what we really loved – our dolls. 'Was it Dad who bought us all those boys' toys for Christmas?' I asked. She nodded meekly in the affirmative. Poor Mum; such pointed behaviour would only have emphasised her sense of failure for not bringing forth sons.

'Well,' I said, gently picking up Mum's hand and changing the subject, 'it's a lovely ring and good for you buying yourself something you really wanted.' Her hands were the same size and shape as my own. We even wrote in the same style. It was a bit like looking into the future and seeing my own hands in my old age.

Although we were not fully aware of the actual extent of Dad's disappointment in our very existence, at least Eileen, Colleen and I had had some experience of him being our father. He was a disciplinarian but could also be generous and protective. Maureen, however, never knew him at all and had perhaps sensed an element of rejection from Mum, especially if Mum believed the disappointment of a fourth daughter had caused her husband's death.

From my work in psychology, I'd learned that our emotional experiences as a child can often affect us later on as adults. I hoped that before Mum died she'd show some genuine love to her youngest daughter, that 'pretty little baby' whose arrival into the world was greeted with so much dismay by both her parents.

12

Each morning upon wakening, I wondered what acts of kindness I could do that day to enhance Mum's life while she was still alive. As the calendar and clock based routines were now significantly reduced, one morning I asked her what she fancied for lunch, anything at all. Her wish was to have a few scallops from the chippy and for me to make her a scallop butty. For Mum, scallops were not of the seafood variety, they were slices of fried potato, also known in the chippies as potato fritters.

In order to make sure I bought the right scallops, Mum described the exact shop where I was to go on Marsh Lane. She said there were two chippies not far from each other on the same side, one called Rongs and the other Dongs. To make things more complicated, Rongs was the right one and Dongs was the wrong one.

So off I went along Marsh Lane only to find that Rongs had closed down but Dongs was still open. Erring on the side of caution, I went to Asda instead and bought some potatoes, lard and white sandwich bread to make scallop butties in exactly the same way Mum had made them when we were children. This meant peeling the potatoes, slicing them into scalloped shapes and frying them in lard. When browned on both sides, they were sprinkled with salt and placed on a slice of white buttered bread. The bread was then folded across the hot scallops to make the original scallop butty. They turned out just as delicious as they'd always been. For me, seeing Mum really enjoying the longed-for scallop butty and to be able to indulge her pleasure with such a simple offering was emotionally uplifting.

One of my acts of kindness, though, was not as well received. As Mum was finding it increasingly difficult to get comfortable, especially in bed, I decided to buy her one of the best ergonomic pillows on the market, which cost just over £100. Placing it on her bed, I hoped it would be a nice surprise for her, but as the saying goes – 'The best laid plans of mice and men often go awry'. Mum hated it, describing the pillow as being like 'a bloody bag of cement' and for me to 'take it away'! At least there was no pretense at politeness!

* * *

On the Sunday morning of the special extra Mother's Day I'd organised, a song began playing over and over in my head. It was a song I didn't particularly like, and it wasn't even the Christmas season when we tend to be more tolerant of such musical annoyances. It was the chorus of *Mistletoe and Wine* by Cliff Richard, complete with the accompanying visuals of Cliff and his female audience waving their arms from side to side as he sang. In keeping with my superstitious upbringing, part of me entertained the idea that this was an omen of bad things to come. My more analytical side tried to work out how that particular song had taken over as an "earworm". Perhaps it had played a part in my dreams that night. Finding no explanation, I splashed my face with cold water and turned on Radio Merseyside for any musical replacement. Anything!

The weather was unusually sunny and mild which made me think Mum might like a little outing after breakfast; maybe we could wander up to the North Park which wasn't far from where she lived. But she didn't want to go anywhere. Venturing outside had now become too much. Even the prospect of looking through the aisles in Asda couldn't lure her back into the wheelchair for an outing.

For a special breakfast in bed, I made Mum a fried egg with bread, accompanied by the usual HP sauce we all used to love, the one which had *By appointment to Her Majesty the Queen* printed on the label, implying that the Queen enjoyed it on her fried eggs too. But things had changed and this sauce now had no place in Mum's new "healthy eating" regime, as she'd read something disturbing about it in a magazine.

'It dries yer blood up that does,' she declared, pointing to the bottle of sauce on the tray. I had no intention of arguing so I returned the sauce to the kitchen cupboard. Mum ate her egg and bread without any fear of her blood drying up that day. For many years we poured this lovely sauce on our eggs and sausages, with no evidence of anyone's blood drying up. In fact, I'd never heard of anybody's cause of death being "blood dried up by sauce" on their death certificate! What sort of magazine had she been reading to give her such ideas?

When Brenda and Laura arrived at 10am to help bathe and dress Mum, I carefully wrapped the Mother's Day present I'd bought. It was a small bottle of perfume called Californian Poppy, a scent Mum had worn when she was younger. I thought it was obsolete until stumbling across it for sale on the internet. Hopefully this would be a lovely surprise for her when she opened the presents from her daughters later that day.

For her Sunday dinner, Mum requested New Zealand lamb with mint sauce (this sauce apparently being OK), roast potatoes and boiled cabbage with gravy. In keeping with tradition, we'd be eating this main meal at 3pm just as we had in the old days. Dessert would be apple crumble and custard.

At midday, I put the lamb in the oven and began to prepare the vegetables. Mum wanted the cabbage to be boiled for at least an hour so it would be really soggy – just how she liked it and how we'd eaten it when we were children.

'All the vitamins are lost in the water when it's been boiled that long,' I said. But she was insistent on being served what she wanted.

'Well, I'll make the gravy with the boiled cabbage water; that way we're not losing out on all the goodness,' I suggested. But no, that wouldn't do, as she wanted ordinary boiled water and Bisto for the gravy – 'like I've always done it'! I saved some of the cabbage water to drink later rather than throw it down the sink. On reflection, I wish I hadn't mentioned the cabbage being over-boiled. For Mum to hear that she'd spent a lifetime throwing out the goodness while serving up the soggy mush wouldn't have been appreciated at that late stage of her life.

It must have been hard for Mum to have her kitchen taken over by somebody else, especially as I was cooking a family Sunday dinner in the same way she'd made it, except of course, we didn't have lamb then; it was usually roast hearts instead. Hearing all the clacking of pan lids and the clatter of plates and cutlery, Mum made a tremendous effort to get up out of her armchair to shuffle into her kitchen to see for herself 'what the hell' was going on in there.

'What's *that* you're drinking?' she asked.

'It's the cabbage water; someone might as well get the vitamins,' I said.

Mum stared at me, wearing an expression of disgust as though she'd caught me drinking my own urine. I told her about the 100-year-old woman who swore that the secret of her good health and longevity was drinking a cup of boiled cabbage water every day. Mum just shook her head in disbelief as I helped her back to her chair. I suppose for her being 91 was bad enough and the idea of spending another nine years drinking cabbage water in order to reach 100 would hold little appeal.

The exertion involved for Mum to walk into the kitchen unaided had taken its toll. Instead of returning to her chair, she wanted to go to bed. Lying down, she began pleading to God, 'Oh God, take me, take me, I've had enough!' She was very weak and clearly fed up with the effort required for just about every physical movement, especially trying to walk on her pitifully thin legs.

When Eileen and Colleen arrived together, Mum preferred to stay in bed rather than sit in the lounge with us. That wasn't a problem, we'd all have our dinner in the bedroom with Mum, so a few extra chairs were brought in. Rather than wait for Maureen to arrive before opening the Mother's Day presents, Eileen presented Mum with a new pair of blue slippers. Uncovering Mum's spindly legs from under the blankets, Eileen put the slippers on her feet, but they were way too big.

'God, they're like bloody canoes! What possessed yer to buy them?' she said, lifting one thin leg up in the air, the slipper dangling precariously off the end of her foot. 'Take them back,' she demanded. 'I won't be wearing *them.*'

Eileen offered to swap them for a smaller size, but was told 'No, don't bother, don't waste yer money, just take them back.' The word 'charming' was mouthed by Eileen accompanied by one raised eyebrow at the effrontery of it all.

Next came Colleen's offering of chocolates: a double layered box of Mum's favourites – Milk Tray. Like her daughters, Mum was a chocolate lover and would normally open the box for sharing, but instead she crinkled her nose, waving the gift away saying, 'They just make phlegm.' Mum's curmudgeonly manner triggered off a round of smirking, especially since I'd been telling my sisters how her attitude had become much more positive lately. Colleen opened the box of chocolates anyway and, phlegm or no phlegm, we helped ourselves.

Then it was my turn. I was sure the Californian Poppy perfume would save the day. I thought I'd triumphed when Mum brightened up on unwrapping the gift saying, 'Oh, I haven't had that for years; it was the most gorgeous smell in the world.' As she struggled to open it, I took it from her, undid the top and lifted the opened bottle of scent to her nose. But her face changed from smiling to frowning within seconds as she sniffed at the perfume. 'That's not it. That's not Californian Poppy.' We all had a sniff and she was right. It was nothing like the original fragrance. How disappointing for her, and to think it had cost me £35.

'You've been duped,' she said, resting her head back on her pillow, and with a long sigh she closed her eyes.

So there we sat like the Three Wise Men, but bearing unwanted gifts. Eileen with her oversized canoes, Colleen with her phlegm-making chocolates and me duped into buying a poor imitation of her favourite scent. At least we could see the funny side of the situation. But our giggling stopped when we heard Mum beginning to groan while looking up at the ceiling, 'Oh God, take me, take me …! What have I done to deserve all this suffering? I don't wanna be here.' It was a distressing situation all right, our mother feeling so miserable on her special day.

'Poor Mum,' I said, turning to my sisters.

'Poor God,' Eileen responded, 'having to listen to that all the time.' Colleen began softly whistling the tune to *Always Look on the Bright Side of Life,* a song Mum wouldn't recognise as she never watched Monty Python films. Eileen joined in whistling the few notes that came after that line. It seemed insensitive of them, but I knew what they'd say if

I offered my thoughts. They'd say Mum had been like this for years. That she would appear to be at death's door one minute and then within seconds she'd be sitting up right as rain wanting to know 'What's in them sandwiches that were just brought in?' Although Mum could often laugh at herself, it wasn't the case on this occasion. She was a very frail old woman and to my mind entitled to some self-pity and certainly to a little compassion from others.

A knocking on the door heralded the arrival of Maureen. She was wearing an orange chiffon scarf wrapped around her head and carrying a bunch of sunflowers. Of all the presents for her to bring that day! She was probably testing things out, as I'd told her over the phone how Mum was now far more flexible and agreeable than she'd been when I first arrived a few months ago. But given what we'd just witnessed with our presents, Maureen was putting herself and her flowers at the mercy of Mum's foul mood. I could just imagine what was to come. No doubt the usual 'Take them away!' and 'You shouldn't have wasted yer money', with Mum looking at the flowers as though being presented with a dead rat.

But it didn't turn out like that at all. On noticing the flowers, Mum's face began to darken, but when she saw it was Maureen holding them, she softened, even smiling and saying it was good to see her. Looking back on this, I believe the talk we had about Maureen's birth and Dad's obsessive longing for a son had indeed been helpful. I also wondered if Mum's aversion to being brought flowers was related to that cheerless time when she was in hospital after giving birth to her fourth daughter.

'Put them in that glass vase under the sink,' Mum requested, 'and stand them over there by the window.'

'What's with the scarf?' Eileen asked Maureen. 'Have you changed your religion or something?' When Maureen removed her scarf we all gasped. Mum asked her if she'd been getting hit again, but no, she'd recently undergone facelift surgery. She had now moved into a house in Warrington with a new boyfriend named Daniel and had a job lined up working in a local restaurant. And for this new life she'd decided to include a new face. In such a very short period of time she'd gone all out to reinvent herself. But the face we were looking at was no improvement on the Maureen we knew. The swelling was asymmetrical and there was a lot of bruising down both sides of her face and neck.

'Is *that* your new face?' Colleen asked incredulously. But Maureen didn't seem too concerned. 'It'll go down in a week or so,' she said confidently. 'It was much worse than this last week.'

'It looks like a bad case of mumps,' Colleen added, as everyone continued staring at Maureen's face.

But Maureen just laughed which made her look even worse, saying, 'Well, that's why I have to wear a scarf, isn't it?' Our little Maureen seemed ever so self-assured, despite her current distorted appearance. Moving to another town and away from Mum seemed to have made a huge difference for her.

'How much did that cost?' Eileen wanted to know.

'Just over £5,000.'

'Good God! You paid £5,000 to look like Quasimodo?' Eileen exclaimed, followed by: 'Where on earth did you find that sort of money?'

'From me new man, Daniel. He paid for it. He's loaded.'

Paying full attention to what she'd been hearing, Mum declared, 'I wouldn't have that done to me for a million pounds! You look like you've had a stroke.' That started the laughing off again amongst her daughters, Maureen included. I could see Mum was beginning to enjoy hearing the laughter of her appreciative audience. 'At least you'll be able to go on a benefit looking like that,' she added, trying to find some upside to the situation along with creating a few more laughs.

It was good that Maureen was laughing along with us, being like one of us and not crumbling under the remarks she was hearing from her family. Colleen, too, could think of some advantages relating to Maureen's new look. 'You could hire yourself out as a professional mourner for unpopular dead people. You could easily start a little business for yourself going around looking like that!' On hearing this Mum began really laughing. She enjoyed a good roar and that was exactly what we were all hoping for to help snap her out of her misery. Maureen knew us well enough to allow her face to be presented as a topic suitable for inducing laughter for Mum. It seemed to be something her daughters had been doing right back from when we were teenagers.

But Mum's laughter soon turned to horror when Colleen accidentally cracked the mirror on the wardrobe carrying in an extra chair for Maureen.

'Oh God, you'll be in for seven years' bad luck now!' she announced. As well as attributing the concept of luck to healthy bowel movements, for Mum, luck could also play a major role in everyday events. She'd always been superstitious, which meant we'd been raised in a household where a parallel universe existed, mainly consisting of Good Luck and Bad Luck. A variety of rituals were used in the hope of influencing these two powers. For example, the act of throwing a pinch of salt over your left shoulder to ward off Bad Luck or hanging up horseshoes as ornaments to attract Good Luck. A bird flying inside a house predicted bad news coming, and an elephant in the house, well, that was the ultimate in Bad Luck, but then it would be, wouldn't it? Breaking a mirror was right up there in the Bad Luck camp, coming as it did with a sentence of seven years of misfortune and no known ritual to ward it off.

Colleen looked alarmed, as though a voodoo bone had been pointed at her, but I was curious about the details of this superstitious nonsense.

'Who actually gets the bad luck? Is it the person who breaks the mirror or the person who owns the mirror?' I asked, as it was Mum's mirror that had been broken by Colleen. Mum, being the self-appointed oracle of the household, answered my question with an air of certainty, informing us that the person who breaks the mirror attracts the penalty. On hearing this, Colleen was put out by the unfairness of it all.

'But I'm only just coming out of seven years of bad luck for the last broken mirror and now there's another lot to get through!' she complained, as though Mum was stating facts rather than merely repeating superstitious twaddle.

'It's just a load of nonsense,' I said. 'All those people who suffered during the war, did they all bring it upon themselves because they all broke mirrors around the same time? And I bet there are loads of people who've broken mirrors and had good luck, so it's all just silly superstitious rubbish.' There, I'd managed to say my piece.

This created a sense of quiet but it didn't rid Colleen of her furrowed brow or stop her biting her lower lip, nor of Mum having the last say, 'But there *is* something in it, that's all I know.'

There was a time some years ago when it was popular for people to visit clairvoyants and spiritualists to find out what the future held. I remember Mum and seven other people paying £12 each for a group sitting with a 'really good' clairvoyant. As far as I could make out, these "gifted" clairvoyants simply asked people certain questions and then determined from their answers what they might like to hear back. But on this particular evening, the clairvoyant neglected to tell Mum anything at all. There wasn't even a John or an Anne from the Other Side conveying any messages whatsoever for her, not even the generic old standbys of 'watch your handbag' or 'eat more greens'. Meanwhile, others in the group were shaking their heads in astonishment at his accuracy as he was 'so absolutely spot on'!

Needless to say, Mum left the session feeling ripped off. All she knew was that this man had earned £96 in cash that night and she hadn't received anything for her money. She confessed to us that she'd contacted the Inland Revenue the following day and told them who this clairvoyant was and what he'd earned that night. As he wasn't likely to have been paying tax on his earnings, the Inland Revenue had said they'd follow up on him. When we heard what Mum had done, we all felt a sense of sympathy toward the clairvoyant and expressed surprise that Mum would do such a thing. Feeling a bit guilty, and in order to justify her actions, she simply declared, 'Well, if he was any good he'd have seen it coming, wouldn't he?'

Following on from the broken mirror incident, I attempted to lighten the mood by returning to the main reason we were there. A celebratory drink was in order. I'd bought some little bottles of Babycham, this being one of the few alcoholic drinks that Mum liked. And so we all congregated in the bedroom, with Mum propped up in her bed, Eileen lounging on the end of the bed and the rest of us sitting on wooden upright chairs brought in from the lounge. With a glass of fizzing Babycham in one hand and a Milk Tray chocolate in the other, we toasted the life of our mother.

'Here's to our lovely mammy,' I said lifting my glass and looking at her, 'and thank you for bringing us up and for giving us such a lovely childhood.' From the corner of my eye I could see some eyebrows were raised higher than the glasses, but that was just their humour.

At first, Mum didn't respond to the toast, but then recalled one by one the many incidents of our childhoods when she had to rush us to the doctors or to the hospital. Apparently, we had a habit of poking things into places where they became lodged. For example, a bead in an ear, a bean up a nose or a lolly-pop stuck in the throat. There was even an incident when Eileen managed to get her foot jammed between the wheel spokes of Dad's bike, and while Mum carried Eileen (who was then three), Dad carried the bicycle wheel which was attached to her foot. And they walked like that all the way to Bootle Hospital.

'You were all bloody nuisances,' she said half jokingly as we laughed at the troubles we'd caused.

'We were probably bored and had nothing else to do but stick beans up our noses and shove our feet in wheel spokes,' Eileen said, and there was probably an element of truth in that.

The New Zealand lamb was so tender it fell off the bone as I carved it. With roast potatoes and very well boiled cabbage, it was a fairly nice Sunday dinner accompanied by Bisto gravy and mint sauce. Not wanting to leave Mum alone during the meal, we remained with her in her bedroom, our plates balanced on our laps while Mum was propped up in bed with her meal on a tray.

Just as I was serving the apple crumble and custard for dessert there was a loud and unexpected knocking at the door. Colleen went to see who was there. Two voices could be heard speaking simultaneously: a man's loud deep voice and a vaguely familiar female voice. The man sounded angry and was asking to see 'the bloody shrink!' Following a worried looking Colleen into the lounge was a large man with greying hair and bulging eyes. Hobbling along behind him was Milly from the ninth floor. The man glowered at Colleen and me as though we owed him money.

'Which one of you is the psychiatrist?' he demanded with spittle flying out of his mouth.

Milly tried to appease him saying, 'No, Arthur, it wasn't like that, love, you've got it wrong.' But Arthur wasn't listening.

'Is it you?' he yelled, pointing at Colleen, who quickly began indicating that 'the bloody shrink' was somebody else.

Eileen and Maureen came out of Mum's bedroom to find out what was going on. The man stared at Maureen's face and then looked at Eileen, obviously not sure what 'a shrink' was supposed to look like.

'I'm a psychologist, not a psychiatrist,' I said. 'What's going on? What's happened?'

'You know what's happened. You've been hypnotising my mother, brainwashing her so that she thinks she's… she's in another world!' While Arthur spoke, Milly continued to tug on her son's arm in an effort to stop him, while simultaneously looking at me and saying, 'Sorry, love.'

Meanwhile, Mum's feeble voice could be heard in the background calling, 'What's going on out there?'

'That was just meditation, a relaxation exercise followed by some guided imagery,' I explained to Arthur. 'There's plenty of scientific evidence to support the benefits of doing both those exercises, and on a regular basis. There's nothing harmful about any of it.'

Turning my attention to Milly, I asked her: 'Have you been upset by doing those relaxation exercises, Milly?'

She shook her head saying no, but before she could explain further Arthur piped up again.

'You know what, I'm gonna report you!' he said, pointing a big finger at my face. 'You shouldn't be doing all that hocus-pocus stuff on old women – my mother and your own elderly mother as well!'

Colleen jumped to my aid. 'We've all been doing it. It just makes you feel relaxed; it's harmless. It's not like what you see on the telly, you know, people jumping about the stage thinking they're rabbits; it's nothing like that.'

Before Arthur could interject, Eileen came forward and stood right in front of him. Looking him in the eye she firmly said, 'I think you'd better leave now or I'm gonna call the police.'

'It's me who'll be ringing the police,' he said, turning around and pulling Milly along with him as he left the flat.

'What's going on out there?' Mum called again before we all went back into the bedroom to explain the encounter with Milly's aggressive son.

The Milly incident left me feeling somewhat floored and embarrassed, wondering if I might have overstepped the professional line.

'He's just an idiot,' Eileen concluded; 'the world's full of them.' Although feeling embarrassed, I was curious as to what Milly had been saying or doing to provoke such a response from her son. Surely imagining that you're dancing to music could only ever be interpreted as a positive mental activity, especially when you can't physically dance anymore.

A gloomy and tense atmosphere descended as we ate our desserts. Mum appeared to be seething, staring ahead with a fierce expression as she ate. Finally she spoke.

'She's a stupid thing that Milly. God knows what she's been telling him.' My sisters agreed he'd obviously over-reacted to whatever it was that Milly had been doing.

'She's probably been telling him that she's with a man in her mind,' Colleen suggested, which momentarily broke the gloom by creating a snort of laughter, adding, 'She probably didn't mention that she was only dancing with him, and he's jumped to the wrong conclusion!' It was heart-warming to be with my tribe, to have my family on my side, each one supportive of me in their own way.

I began to wonder if Milly's imagination really had gone into overdrive and moved beyond dancing to something else. That's the thing with the mind – you can do anything or go anywhere without it having any basis in reality. But even if Milly had hit it off with her imaginary dancing partner, so what? We're all capable of enjoying a fantasy, regardless of age.

By the time my sisters left, and Mum had fallen asleep for the night, I was still feeling a little uneasy over what Milly's son had threatened. The last thing I wanted was to have to go back to New Zealand and not be in Liverpool caring for Mum at this stage of her life. Before getting into bed I had my usual last check for emails on my mobile phone. There was a message from Maggie the house-sitter back home in New Zealand telling me that Puzz was dead. My beautiful cat had been found dead, curled up in his favourite chair. Tears began to fall as my emotions changed from apprehension about the Milly incident to sadness for the loss of my lovely Puzz. To think I'd never see him or stroke his soft fur ever again.

What a day it had been. To be threatened by Milly's son as though I were some depraved criminal preying on old women and now Puzz dead. I felt so drained I even entertained the idea that somehow the deity responsible for organising Colleen's allotted extra seven years of bad luck had become confused, and the penalty imposed for breaking the mirror had been visited upon me instead.

That night, as I lay in bed meditating to help me fall asleep, somewhere in the far reaches of my mind I could hear the faint but distinct echoes of that song – *Mistletoe and Wine*!

13

The following day during breakfast, I told Mum about Puzz being found curled up dead in his favourite armchair. He was over sixteen, a good age for a cat. Maggie hadn't recognised that he was dead, as he slept a lot of the time, and it wasn't until she touched his stiff cold body that she realised he must have died in his sleep during the night.

'Was it sick?' Mum asked.

'No, he was fine. He had a good appetite, enjoyed his food. He was just old.'

'A lucky cat, then,' she concluded, quickly changing the subject to the problem of her toenails. They were too long and catching on the sheets when she was in bed. As she wore socks a lot of the time, I hadn't noticed this problem.

'Would you like me to cut them for you, Mum?' Although she didn't seem too keen, she removed a sock to let me have a go at one foot. Picking up the scissors I carefully assessed the situation. The toenails certainly looked way too long and seemed to have been growing in all different directions rather than straight. Gently lifting her left foot on to my lap, I held her big toe between my fingers while holding the scissors in my other hand. But before the scissors had made any contact with her toenail she was grimacing, crying out, 'Oh God! Stop! Stop! It's hurting!'

'Mum, I haven't even started cutting them yet.'

But she didn't want me to continue and, to be honest, I was pleased. It didn't look an easy task for anybody, especially with her hypersensitivity.

I'd seen this type of anticipatory pain reaction before in people about to have blood taken, cringing and flinching, anticipating pain before any needle has been inserted. Interestingly, current research suggests that people with red hair (Mum's hair was auburn before it turned grey) are more sensitive to pain than the average person and, looking back, Mum's reactions usually were over the top and very verbal, even with low levels of discomfort.

When Laura arrived on her own (Brenda being off sick that day), I suggested she might like to have a go at cutting Mum's toenails. Looking at her watch, obviously worried about her busy schedule with Brenda being away, she agreed to help out anyway. Sitting in the chair with her one sock off, Mum looked a pitiful sight. I could see she was on high alert of Laura and any pair of scissors coming near her feet.

'Come on, Lizzie love,' Laura said, looking at Mum, 'let's get those nails cut nice and short for yer.' Without waiting for Mum to object, Laura knelt down and got stuck into the task at hand. This time the scissors were actually making contact but, with the toenail being very hard and horn-like, Laura wasn't making much progress. Suddenly Mum let out a loud screech and told Laura to 'Get off! You're not a professional!' Rolling her eyes in the air, Laura put the scissors down and helped Mum into the bathroom for her shower.

It was around this time I'd given up suspecting Laura of stealing the money, instead believing that my sisters were probably right. The idea of somebody dipping into Mum's savings was more than likely created by a calculating error made early on in her counting. At least the total had remained the same for a long time now since no new money had been added.

But now we had a new problem involving toenails. It was Maureen who'd previously looked after Mum's pedicure needs but I didn't fancy asking her to come all the way from Warrington to cut a few toenails. Instead I rang a local chiropodist. He said he'd try to make it later that week but would slot her in earlier if he received any cancellations. At least Mum couldn't say he wasn't a professional toenail trimmer.

On the Friday morning, the chiropodist arrived full of busyness and importance carrying his black leather bag, no doubt full of heavy duty equipment ready to tackle the most difficult of toenails. With his head held high, he sauntered into the lounge with all the eagerness of a fox terrier. But there was no way in the world that Mum was going to have her nails cut on a Friday. According to the old English rhyme, 'Cut them on Friday you cut them for sorrow'. She asked him to come back on Monday ('for health') or failing that on Tuesday ('for wealth') but never on a Friday! It was the old superstitious nonsense once again calling the shots in Mum's everyday life.

As the chiropodist was leaving without even getting to open his bag, Mum offered him a piece of advice, 'If I was doing your job, I'd make sure that Fridays were me days off and I'd work Saturdays instead.' These words of wisdom would make some sense if you were steeped in superstition as much as she was, as according to the rhyme – 'Cut them on Saturday, you'll meet your true love tomorrow'. How quaint; however, something had to rhyme with sorrow! Strangely enough, all through my life I'd never cut my nails on a Friday, just in case. You don't take any chances when it comes to such a heavily laden emotion as sorrow.

Regardless of any toenails having been cut on a Friday or not, a few days later Colleen phoned to tell us her old dog Lord Rufus had died. He had slithered off the sofa one last time, and when Colleen came home from work she found him lying dead on the cushions below. You'd think the other pets might have been alarmed or even curious about their dead companion on the floor, but no, according to Colleen it was just business as usual, their focus being on what new morsels she had brought home for them. Miss Piggy had remained stretched out on the sofa not showing a hint of concern for her old couch crony lying lifeless just below her. Colleen, however, was very upset. She loved her animals and finding one of her dogs like that was a shock, even though he'd lived to a ripe old age.

The death of Rufus created a sense of foreboding in more ways than one. For Colleen, it marked the start of the new round of Seven Years' Bad Luck, but according to Mum it was also an omen.

'Oh God,' she said in a whispering doom-filled voice,

'deaths always go in threes: your cat, now the dog… ' By the fearful expression on her face she didn't need to say who she thought the third death would be. An old cat, an old dog, and what next? Perhaps an old woman?

This apparent fear of death was a far cry from the begging plea 'Take me, take me' but we humans can be complicated creatures, pushed around by our conflicting emotions. A part of Mum wanted to go but I think another part of her wanted to stay. However, a peaceful and painless death after a good long life would surely be the jackpot.

'Those animals just died in their sleep after very good innings,' I said, 'and wouldn't it be great if we could all go like that when the time comes?' Mum wasn't responding, so I continued my railings against superstition. 'I'd say that's what you call *good* luck… isn't it, Mum?' Mum nodded meekly, agreeing that it was. But she seemed to be holding on to darker thoughts. She didn't say any more about omens but simply requested a cup of tea.

I also was conflicted over Mum dying. I hoped she would get her wish to die soon without any suffering. I could see that life for her was becoming too hard. But I also didn't want her to die just yet. I was getting to know her now and, though she could be frustrating at times, I really loved her and valued our time together. I even caught myself hoping that Colleen's other dog, Miss Piggy, would die soon so that Mum wouldn't feel as though the Sword of Damocles was hanging over *her* head because of the superstitious idea that death comes in threes.

But Miss Piggy wasn't going anywhere soon. She now had the luxury of the whole couch to herself and that meant she could really stretch out in comfort. No more of Rufus's coarse terrier coat prickling her smooth fat belly. That dog loved her home comforts and would be around for a while yet.

* * *

It was approaching late summer in Liverpool and the days were already becoming cooler with a hint of autumn in the air. Autumn, although the most beautiful of seasons, brings a tinge of sadness, underlining the fact that summer is over and winter will soon be on its way.

One Saturday morning, while Colleen and Eileen dropped by after their shopping at Asda, Maureen also paid a visit to Mum's flat. The swelling and bruising from the cosmetic surgery had now disappeared and her face was looking good. In fact, she looked almost ten years younger and nobody could accuse her of looking like Quasimodo now. On the contrary, Maureen looked beautiful. But on closer inspection, something wasn't quite right. There was a small cut on her lower lip that wasn't anything to do with the facelift surgery. It was Eileen who jumped to the conclusion that she was being hit again, this time by her new man Daniel. In Eileen's uniquely diplomatic way, she asked Maureen if she'd undergone more cosmetic surgery, this time on her mouth.

'You haven't had one of those awful trout mouths done, have you?' she asked pointing at Maureen's cut lip. Maureen explained that her new puppy, Wilfred, had jumped up and accidentally knocked her mouth. But

Eileen wasn't buying that as she'd also noticed scratches on Maureen's hands.

'Wilfred must have sharp claws; look at your hands!'

'That wasn't the dog, that's from our new kitten Tigger,' Maureen assured her. 'He's all over the place, scratching everything, including hands.' She went on to inform us that since moving to Warringon, her and Daniel had adopted the pets as neither of them had children, so the animals were their fur children.

'Have you got any photos of these pets?' Eileen asked, obviously not reassured by Maureen's explanation. Looking at her mobile phone to check for photos, Maureen said no she didn't, that she must have taken them all on her proper camera.

Colleen appeared from the kitchen carrying a tray of tea and biscuits. On hearing that Maureen now had two new pets, she wanted to know everything about them; their breed and colour; what ages they were. She didn't think to ask Maureen anything about how she was, but then that was Colleen. She was still getting over losing Rufus, and I was pleased to have successfully talked her out of taking on any new canine replacement just yet. Colleen assured Maureen that if Wilfred was ever 'too much trouble' then she was happy to take him.

'Oh no, we really love having our pets. They're a bit naughty at times, but they're still young,' Maureen replied, like a proud new parent discussing her children in a mothers' group.

Maureen looked and sounded very happy. The new wealthy boyfriend and her new face had obviously helped raise her self-esteem. Hopefully Daniel would care for her and be that loving partner she'd never known. Eileen, however, was still uneasy about it all. Sitting quietly with a worried expression and pursed lips she studied her younger sister. Having been in New Zealand for many years, I'd never seen Maureen's face or body after she'd been beaten by her ex-husband but the others had, therefore it was understandable that somebody might be concerned about the same thing happening again.

Later that morning, after spending some time talking to Mum about her new house in Warrington, Maureen left to go home. Eileen suspected the story about pets causing Maureen's wounds was 'another cover up' just like the tripping up on mats and walking into doors that were supposed to account for all the black eyes, cuts and bruises when she was married to The Brute.

'I don't think she'd put herself through that again,' I said, 'and besides, most men aren't violent; most men just want what we all want, to love and be loved. Maureen was just unlucky enough to marry a bad one.' Colleen agreed with me but took a different tack to arrive at the same place.

'She wouldn't spend all that money on a new face just to have someone undo it all.' But Eileen was insistent that we should go and look at Maureen's house and meet this new rich boyfriend and find out what was really going on. However, we couldn't just turn up without an invitation and, besides, none of us knew the address apart from it being somewhere in Warrington.

After a short silence, Eileen's mind was made up. 'You know what they say, "Evil triumphs when good men do nothing" so we need to do something.' She would certainly make a good revolutionary but, given the situation, there was nothing to suggest any evil was at work.

'We could say we wanted to see her new pets, and check this Daniel out while we're there,' Colleen suggested.

'I don't think she's got any pets,' Eileen affirmed, 'and if *that* turns out to be the case, then you know what's really going on.'

And so it was decided that I'd phone Maureen in the morning and ask if Eileen and I could come and see her new house and pets later that day. As it would be a Sunday, Daniel would likely be there and we could get to meet him. One of us would need to stay with Mum so Colleen volunteered to do that as well as cook her Sunday dinner, allowing me a chance to get out and about in Warrington, a place I'd never been to.

That Saturday evening Mum had a lovely time with the music and her mind-dancing. It was heart-lifting to see her smiling again as I sat on the end of her bed while she returned to the dance hall of her youth. In my imagination too, I could see her waltzing around the ballroom in that red and white dress, her slim waist held firmly by the charming Silver Fox. When she indicated she'd had enough, which was usually signalled by a little wave of her hand, I stopped the music and we just sat in silence for a bit.

'Maureen looked very well, didn't she?' Mum said at last. I was hoping the cut lip hadn't been noticed as I didn't want Mum worrying about the same scenario that had gripped Eileen. I told Mum that Colleen would be staying with her tomorrow while Eileen and I went to visit Maureen to have a look at her new house and her new man.

'I wish I could come,' she said in a wistful little voice.

'Well, shall we see if you can, Mum?' I suggested, immediately realising the futility of such an idea.

'No, I wouldn't be up to it,' she said sadly.

'I tell you what, I'll take some photos while I'm there and you can look at them when I get back.' After a short contemplative silence Mum made a specific request of me.

'Maureen told me she had a nice back garden. Can you take a picture of that for me?' I remembered Mum's regret that she'd never had a little garden of her own, a place where she could sit and enjoy a bit of sunshine. It didn't seem much to ask after a lifetime of toil. The emotion of it caught in my throat, causing me to reach out and touch her gently on the arm. I'd have liked to have hugged her but she was now too frail for that.

'I'll make sure I take some good photos for you.' As I spoke I could feel my breath rising up between the words like tiny staccato sobs from deep within my body.

'Yes, I bet she'll have a lovely garden, Mum.'

14

Maureen's new home was a small brick terraced house situated right in the middle of a block of similar houses. While I knocked on the door, Eileen stood on tiptoes trying to peer through the front window. When Maureen opened the door, and before we could even say hello, a boisterous young black dog came bouncing up the hall, his tail wagging frantically as he jumped up against us, almost knocking me over. He seemed very big and heavy for such a youngster. Once inside and after much licking and sniffing, he finally settled down. Maureen and Daniel had adopted Wilfred from an animal shelter where he'd been on Death Row. He was of uncertain heritage, but from the look of his paws he was going to be a big dog. It was easy to see how such an enthusiastic animal could accidentally bang Maureen in the mouth. I'd only been there a few minutes and already my left leg was hurting where he'd jumped up at me.

From the outside, the house seemed small, but it was surprisingly spacious inside despite having only two bedrooms. As Maureen showed us around, it became obvious she was very proud of her new home. A multitude of scatter cushions and throws, all in different patterns, fabrics and colours, dominated the couch in the lounge. How anybody was supposed to sit on such a couch without disturbing the whole extravaganza, I didn't know. I'd seen this sort of display before in those perfect home type magazines in which aesthetics completely override practicality. No longer a piece of furniture for human bums to sit on, Maureen's couch had become something else. A showpiece for cushions and throws.

I wasn't the only one intrigued by the voluminous array of cushions. Eileen's pursed lips and raised eyebrow silently expressed her disapproval. She poured scorn on such trends and those who blindly followed them. But I was pleased for Maureen, who was obviously now trying to create a nest of her own. Perhaps the vibrant excess of cushions was an over-reaction to living with Mum and her two beige-coloured cushions for the last few years.

A man with a dark curly forelock came in from the back garden. The sleeves of his blue checkered shirt were rolled up and he was carrying a spade. He looked a bit younger than Maureen but it was hard to tell how old he was, and with warm dark eyes and a cheerful expression there was certainly nothing brute-like about him. All he needed were drainpipe trousers and winkle-picker shoes to look as though he'd just stumbled out of the 1950s.

'This is Daniel,' Maureen said smiling proudly. Before extending a hand out to greet us, he quickly wiped his hands on his trousers.

'This is Eileen,' Maureen continued, 'and this is Kathleen… er, I mean Katherine.' Daniel's handshake was something between a gentle and a firm grip. Definitely not floppy and weak, nor was it an iron-like grasp. Some people believe you can judge a person by their handshake. If so, then this one indicated a balanced nature.

'Oh, just call her our Ka-leen,' Eileen quipped. 'She much prefers that.'

'Take no notice of her,' I said; 'you can call me Katherine.' Daniel navigated his way around this awkward situation by simply not mentioning any names for the rest of the time we were there.

Maureen and Daniel showed us their small back garden where there was a border of flowering plants around a tiny square lawn. In a corner at one end was a garden swing. At the other end, a couple of green plastic chairs were placed against the back door. I took plenty of photos for Mum, knowing she would have loved such a garden. What looked like an orange cushion on the garden swing suddenly began to move. It was the ginger kitten, Tigger. Like most young cats, he was full of life, everything from chasing insects to running up and down the curtains in the house. Though much smaller than the dog, Tigger was already the boss.

We followed Maureen upstairs as she showed us the rest of the house. In the main bedroom, we came across another example of how a modern furnishing trend had influenced Maureen's ideas of home decor. On the bed a mountain of pillows and cushions, all of different shapes, colours, fabrics and sizes, were piled one on top of the other from the headboard right down to the middle of the bed.

On encountering such a display, Eileen could no longer stay quiet. Tut-tutting and waving a hand across the bed she asked, 'What's the point of all this?' Maureen and I started to laugh as Eileen continued her rant. 'How many heads do you think people have? How on earth could anybody get in that bed?' I could see Eileen's point all right, but it was Maureen's bed in Maureen's house. I felt a bit sorry for her, as Eileen could be very insensitive at times, however, it seemed that Maureen could now speak up for herself.

'It's just soft furnishings, part of the new modern look. I think it makes the bed look really nice and all the colours liven up the room.'

'But it's lost its function,' Eileen argued; 'it's not a bed anymore, is it? It's the same with your settee downstairs. It's not for sitting on anymore, just as this isn't for lying on!'

Eileen seemed to be over-stating her case and I wished she'd just let it go, but she wouldn't. She was like a dog with a bone.

'Shall we see if we can lie down on it, then?' Eileen said, looking at me as the suitable volunteer. At this time Daniel entered the room along with the dog.

'They're gonna see if they can lie down on the bed,' Maureen explained to Daniel.

'Are you that tired already?' he asked, unaware of the issue at hand. Eileen gladly repeated her opinion regarding the pillows and cushions. She was enjoying the situation, ordering me to 'come on' and 'let's pretend we're exhausted and we suddenly want to lie down on this nice comfy bed'. To demonstrate her point, on the count of three Eileen and I were to lie down on the bed as it was. 'One… two… ' She looked at me to make sure I was in on the demonstration, and on the count of three Eileen and I threw our bodies on to the bed. It was like being submerged in a bubble bath of pillows. Our heads disappeared under the silky fabrics where we were stifled by velvet tassels and semi-smothered by an army of soft furnishings. We were like two big beetles floundering on our backs as cushions and pillows flew in all directions. Within seconds the dog joined in the fun on the bed, powering over us with his big paws.

After a good laugh, and with Eileen feeling triumphant that she'd proven her point, we all went downstairs. 'Have a seat on the sofa,' Maureen suggested with a smile. At least she was taking it all in good spirits. Instead of taking up the challenge of trying to sit on the couch, we sat at the table for our afternoon tea and cakes while we chatted with Daniel and Maureen. Eileen seemed to have forgotten the reason she'd insisted on coming in the first place. If only the kitten would scratch her so as to remove all suspicion about Maureen being physically hurt by her new partner. But Eileen was only a dog-lover. She had no time for cats and avoided any contact with the kitten.

Daniel wasn't anything like I'd imagined him to be. He certainly didn't come across as being the wealthy man Maureen had described. When I asked him what he did for a living, he said he was currently between jobs but was hoping to secure some landscaping work soon. I was also surprised to learn that their little terraced house was rented rather than owned. But whether he was "loaded" or not, Daniel seemed to be a fairly genuine human being.

Before heading back to Liverpool, we took Wilfred for

a walk in the nearby cemetery, this being the only bit of green space in the area. It was so good to feel a dog at the end of a lead again. Before she became too old, I used to walk my dog Cindy twice a day in New Zealand. I enjoyed watching her sniff about and how things unnoticed by humans were exciting to her. Dogs certainly know how to fully experience their world, remaining right in the moment of their lives.

As we walked along the cemetery path with gravestones on either side of us, this environment provided a stark reminder of how precious it is to be alive. Life. Our individual specks of time on this planet. Some of the gravestones were from previous centuries with lichen covering the names along with the dates of birth and death of those lying beneath the ground. These were people who'd experienced hopes and disappointments, times of happiness and times of sadness. People just like us.

My pondering over human existence was interrupted by the others laughing as the dog did a quick circular movement before humping his back in that very conspicuous way that dogs do when having a poo. According to Maureen, Wilfred liked to do his business every day on the same grave, which happened to be the resting place of Annie Smith, a woman who'd died over 120 years ago. Why he chose this grave from all the hundreds of others around was considered mysterious. Maureen wondered if Annie Smith might have been Wilfred's previous owner in the dog's previous life, that there must be some connection we just didn't understand. From my perspective at that time, given a dog's superior sense of smell and the canine predilection for routine, it wasn't really mysterious, just open to all sorts of extravagant hypotheses.

Walking back to Maureen's house, Eileen chatted with Daniel, who now had Wilfred on the lead. Maureen and I walked behind them. I could see how gentle Daniel was with the dog, stopping to allow him time to sniff at a bush without pulling him along. I felt sure Maureen would be safe with this man.

'He seems really nice, Maureen,' I said, looking ahead at Daniel.

'Yeh, he is. Once he gets a job we'll be OK. It's hard at the moment with just me working, especially with the extra expenses for the pets.' What Maureen was saying seemed incongruous with what she'd told us previously. Why would an unemployed man, who was hoping to find work soon, pay all that money for her to have cosmetic surgery? It didn't add up.

But just as I was about to inquire on this anomaly, my mobile phone rang. It was Colleen. She sounded frantic as she told us that Mum wouldn't wake up, that she'd had to call the emergency doctor out. Upon hearing this, Eileen and I quickly said goodbye to Maureen, who now had Daniel's comforting arm around her shoulders. As we drove off we promised Maureen we'd let her know what was happening with Mum just as soon as we could. On the trip back to Liverpool, Eileen and I hardly spoke. This was not how I envisaged Mum dying, not when I wasn't even there.

By the time we arrived back at Marsh Lane, the doctor had been and gone and Mum was described as feeling comfortable. Colleen, however, was still a bit shaky, especially when recalling how she'd believed that this time Mum really had died.

During the following weeks, Mum remained in her bed for most of the time. Amazingly, her spindle-thin legs had become even thinner and, despite having the help of a carer on either side of her, she could no longer walk to the bathroom without distress. A commode was set up in the bedroom to make toileting easier.

'It's like having your own little en suite, Mum,' I said referring to the commode. But she didn't laugh. On reflection, she probably didn't know what an en suite was. For her, simply having an inside toilet was considered the height of luxury compared to an outside "lavvy" which was all she'd known for much of her life. The comforts of having a proper bathroom and kitchen with hot running water for the last 28 years were aspects of her life she'd always appreciated and had never taken for granted.

Another obviously important facet of Mum's life was frugality. The relentless penny-pinching, scrimping and saving were imprinted on her psyche as necessary for survival. Like many of her generation, it was important to have some money put by for the inevitable rainy day. She often evaluated the price of things for sale against a 1950s' yardstick, so it wasn't surprising when she complained about paying £12 for a packet of padded knickers, this being 'more than a week's wages!', even though they would make life more comfortable and safer for her, as she wouldn't have to get up in the night if she needed to go to the toilet. On occasions she could even be concerned about how much toilet paper the carers tore off the roll for her to use – 'Good God, not *that* much!'

This past-focused mindset also influenced her ideas of what constituted a good holiday. For example, when one of her grandsons was off to India for four weeks, she couldn't understand it, not when the Blackpool lights would soon be switched on and he could have 'a lovely outing on a coach trip' to see them. The world had now become a very different place and at times a very confusing place for Mum.

For the first time in her life she stopped watching *Coronation Street*. I'd set up a television set in her bedroom especially so she could continue to watch her favourite programme, but she'd 'lost all interest'. It was the same with the horse-racing. She no longer had enough mental energy to maintain the required focus. Although we still attempted the dancing imagery, more often than not she'd fall asleep while the music was still playing. One of the few remaining distractions she could still tolerate was the radio, which I'd positioned on the small table next to her bed so she could listen to her beloved Radio Merseyside.

As she could no longer walk anywhere without help, her counting of the hidden money had stopped. She didn't seem too worried about this, saying she could keep a good eye on it where she was, so I guessed it must have been somewhere close by her bed. I asked her if she would like me to count it for her, but no, she said she was happy to just leave it alone for now.

Julie, who continued to keep a regular eye on Mum, commented on how amazing it was that she was still alive, given how thin and weak she'd become. Each morning, I now cut Mum's toast into very small pieces and helped her to sip her tea from a baby bottle. To see her deteriorate at this rate was heart-breaking. Although she still managed to eat breakfast, her appetite waned during the rest of the day as the effort of eating and drinking became exhausting for her. It's been claimed that old age is like a second childhood. Mum may have been fed like a baby and helped with her toileting, but there was no future growth ahead for her as there would be with a child. Only decline. Wrinkled skin rather than firm young skin. Blank tired eyes rather than curious lively eyes. She was now helpless, and I tried to keep her dignity intact as much as possible, engaging with her as an adult rather than resorting to scolding and patronising her as though she were a naughty toddler the way some people do when interacting with the elderly.

As her appetite decreased, the frequency of Mum's pleading to the ceiling with clasped hands increased. 'God, what have I done to deserve this? I've never smoked, I've always eaten good healthy food, I've never drunk alcohol the way others have… Why am I being punished like this?' She seemed genuinely puzzled as she continued, 'All the people I grew up with are long gone, and here's me left lingering like this.' She couldn't see the irony in what she was saying as she tried to persuade God that she'd been overlooked and that her rights were being violated. For Mum, it was as though she'd fallen through the cracks of heaven's bureaucratic records system.

In an effort to shift Mum away from thinking like this, I raised the topic of gratitude. How we can be grateful for all the little things in life along with the big things. Taking a Big Picture view of life, she simply didn't want to be here anymore, so being grateful for each new day and the actual experience and wonder of being alive on this planet was of no value or inspiration to her. On the contrary, she described being disappointed to wake up each morning as it meant having to endure yet another day. She was uncomfortable, she'd lost her independence and she was fed up with it all.

Trying to encourage Mum to focus on being grateful for small things seemed a little more hopeful than trying to use the Big Picture approach, but not much. I moved her bed around to face the window so she could see the outside world. In the distance there was the tower of Saint John's, the church where she'd been baptized and where she wanted to have her funeral service. I tried to engage her in her favourite topics of conversation, which always involved the past, the people she knew, the humorous stories, but her interest couldn't be sustained for longer than a few minutes before the wailing began. Her repetitive pleading to God to 'Take me, take me!' was followed by 'What have I done to deserve this?' Needless to say, it was an extremely distressing time for her and it was heart-wrenching for me to see her like that.

Eventually, even the sound of the radio could no longer be tolerated so I put it back in the lounge. The medication she was now on caused her to become even more drowsy and a lot of her time was spent drifting in and out of sleep. There was no getting away from the fact that Mum really was nearing the end of her life, but perhaps not as fast as she would have liked. I moved the single bed from my room into her room so that I could be with her during the night as well as the day. And so the waiting had begun for the final curtain to fall.

Looking out of the window in the lounge, I could see the old black stone building that was once Bootle Town Hall in the distance. This was where Mum once had a cleaning job. To the right were the docks where Dad had worked up to a few weeks before he died. To the left I could see the railway station at Marsh Lane, the trains still travelling back and forth on the Liverpool Central to Southport line. Although they were faster and quieter now, the journey itself was much the same as it had been in the 1950s and 1960s during the family days out to Southport on bank holidays. All the city children would become excited upon seeing cows and sheep in the fields as the train passed through the more rural areas to the north of Liverpool. Gazing out of the window of Mum's lounge that day was like looking through a kaleidoscope of shifting memories, my mind sliding back to images of times gone by and then returning to the present moment.

Just to complete the poignancy of that moment, a song called *Days* by The Kinks, began playing on the radio. The words seemed very relevant to what I was experiencing and the hot tears came quickly. It was too much. Turning the radio off, I dried my face and checked on Mum in the bedroom. She was awake so I took the opportunity of taking her thin little hand and thanking her for bringing me into the world, for caring for me as a child and for giving me a very happy and secure childhood. I told her how grateful I was for that childhood, that those days had built a foundation for me to function well in the world as an adult. What made me even more grateful was that I now knew from our conversations over the last few months just how much effort and sacrifice the wife and mothering role had been for her.

Mum seemed to take it all in. Then in a small voice she thanked me for what I'd been doing to make life easier for her these last few months.

'Oh Mum, this is nothing compared to what you've done for me. Nothing!'

Immediately, the familiar feeling of guilt washed over me like an ocean wave crashing on to rocks. Guilty. Yes, I was guilty of being in New Zealand all those years, allowing thousands of miles to distance and alienate myself from my family. How our lives turn out to be so different to the way we imagined they'd be. When it comes to emigrating, the loss is shared by the past, present and future generations of a family.

While Mum was still awake I asked her if there was anything she would like me to do for her, anything at all. Her answer surprised me.

'A candle,' she said. 'If you could light a candle for me.' At first I thought she wanted me to buy her a candle to light in the room for her, but no, it was for after her death. She wanted me to light a candle for her in Saint John's Church.

'Of course I will, Mum. I promise you I'll do that.'

'There's something else I'd like,' she said. 'I'd like to say sorry to Maureen… for the way I've treated her.'

'I'll make sure you get the opportunity to do that, Mum. I'll organise for her to come round and spend some time with you.'

She said she didn't want anything more. Closing her eyes, she then drifted back to sleep.

Ringing my sisters, I told them that Mum wouldn't last long now, maybe not even the week. Colleen and Maureen said they'd come round the next day, but not without reminding me how they'd been through this same deathbed situation several times over the last few years.

Along with having a boiled egg on hand, Eileen suggested I shouldn't bother contacting the priest, as there would be an understandable reluctance on his part to come over again as he'd administered the Last Rights for Mum several times over the previous year. Although I hadn't been there to witness Mum's miraculous recoveries as my sisters had, I believed that this time it really was different.

15

On the following morning when the carers left, Eileen and Colleen arrived first, followed shortly by Maureen. As Mum's four daughters gathered in the lounge ready to formally farewell our mother, we discussed the order in which each of us would go into the bedroom to say a personal goodbye.

Eileen wanted to go first in order to 'witness' Mum agreeing to 'accept Jesus into her heart' so that when she died she'd then be eligible for a special resurrection at the sound of the holy trumpet call. This trumpet heralded in the Second Coming, when Mum would rise up out of her grave, along with all other Christians, to be with Jesus and the Heavenly Host. Opening her bag, Eileen pulled out the Bible she'd brought along for Mum to swear on.

'Eileen, I don't think you should be pressuring her to do that sort of thing when she's so weak and unwell,' I said. Colleen and Maureen agreed that the last thing Mum needed right now was somebody making religious demands of her.

'But there's no better time than now if she's about to die. It's all here in the Scriptures. If she dies without accepting Christ into her heart, she'll go to hell, everlasting torment! Is that what you want for her?' Eileen looked genuinely concerned, and I suppose if anybody really believed such a thing then of course they would feel concerned.

'I don't think God would be cruel like that. She hasn't been *that* bad,' Colleen reasoned, looking towards Maureen for support. 'She hasn't murdered anyone and I don't think she's ever stolen anything.'

'Well, it's true she's been mean in a lot of different ways,' Maureen said, looking at Eileen holding her Bible, 'but I think a priest would be more suitable than all that.'

'Look, I didn't write the Scriptures, it's the word of God and that's what we have to accept,' Eileen explained, opening her Holy Book to show us the printed words, flicking through the pages as though that were proof enough to support her claims.

'So, you think us lot here are all going to hell?' I asked.

'It's not up to me to decide that, but if you die without accepting the Christian faith then that's probably where you'll go.'

'I really don't think you should be talking about hell and trumpets to Mum when she's sick like that. It'd be cruel. It doesn't make sense,' I said, continuing, 'If God's supposed to be a loving father, he wouldn't be that hung up on torturing his own children. Even a mediocre human father wouldn't conjure up everlasting pain and burning for his daughter because she didn't swear allegiance to him on a book.'

'Our dad gave us a good belting but he always bought us chocolates the next night to make up for it,' Colleen added. 'He wouldn't have put us in hell… not like that.'

But Eileen's Bible remained firmly in her hand as she headed towards Mum's bedroom. 'Leave her alone!' I shouted, while attempting to hold her back. But she was as strong as a bull and pulled away, very determined that Mum would not be going to hell, not while she was around.

In the bedroom, Eileen knelt down next to Mum and began her religious spiel. I closed the door feeling disgusted. I didn't want to create a row while Mum lay there dying.

Returning to the topic at hand, Colleen concluded, 'If she does die, she'll still be around in spirit.' She was trying to salvage something from what had become a heated sibling argument over religion, a situation lacking in the usual family humour. Maureen agreed with Colleen, saying that we'd all return to the spirit world when we died and be able to see things more clearly then.

'Well, that's fairly debatable,' I said, 'but it's one up on fire and brimstone. How can Eileen believe all that, peddling teachings from the Dark Ages, from a time when people accepted that the earth was flat?'

'Are you trying to say that the earth's not flat?' Colleen asked, attempting to lighten up the atmosphere. However, given what I'd just heard from each of my sisters, I couldn't really be sure she was joking!

After a few minutes, Eileen came out of Mum's bedroom. She said there had been no resistance from Mum to put her hand on the Bible and agree with what was required. Eileen looked as though an apology was in order.

'But anybody would do that, wouldn't they? Just say whatever's required for a bit of peace or… or for a bit of insurance, you know, just in case.' I shook my head in disbelief.

But Eileen was now the White Knight, a saver of souls, and disregarded the opinions of Philistines.

What was supposed to have been a special time for us to take the opportunity to say our individual farewells to Mum was going badly awry. We all sat awkwardly and silently in the lounge until Eileen stood up saying, 'Well, I'm off now.' She then asked Colleen if she wanted a lift home, which she did. But before they left I asked Colleen if she'd like to say goodbye to Mum as it just might be the last time she'd get the chance.

'Tara, Mum, we're off now,' she called into the bedroom. It wasn't how a final farewell to a dying mother was meant to be. Perhaps she really did expect Mum to recover, even though anybody could see it would be unlikely she'd last the week.

With just Maureen and me left, it was an opportunity to fulfil Mum's request for her to apologise to her youngest daughter before she died. However, Maureen said she didn't want an apology, that it would be 'too little, too late'. Her bitterness surprised and saddened me.

'Just let Mum get it off her chest, so she can go in peace. You don't even have to say anything, just nod or touch her hand so she knows that you've heard her.' But Maureen didn't want to.

'Well, just pretend to accept the apology; you don't have to mean it. Do it as an act of kindness. Could you do it for me, then, if not for Mum? Go on… Please.' I sounded pathetic but Maureen finally agreed and I thanked her profusely.

Going into the bedroom, I gently bent over Mum to let her know that Maureen was here to speak to her, but she'd fallen asleep.

'Don't wake her up,' Maureen said. 'You can tell her that I'll call again soon.'

Picking up her coat and bag, she hurried off, asking to be kept informed if Mum got any worse.

Did any of them love her? Their own mother? With Eileen it appeared to be all about rules and dogma rather than love. In some ways Colleen seemed afraid of Mum, often avoiding any chance to be emotionally intimate with her. And as for Maureen, well, I don't think she even liked Mum. Did I love my mother? I certainly felt a fierce affection for her, so I guess you could call that love. What a sad time it was in so many different ways.

About fifteen minutes later Maureen came back, saying she'd left her mobile phone on the kitchen bench. Unfortunately, Mum was still asleep, but Maureen wanted to sit with her anyway, so she'd be there should she wake up. The door was closed to allow privacy. I tried to listen but couldn't hear anybody speaking in there, and after about five minutes Maureen came out.

Although Mum had remained asleep, Maureen seemed a lot more chirpy than she had been earlier. I wondered if seeing how weak and helpless Mum now was had lessened her resentment. While standing by the window looking out, to determine whether or not it was raining, in the reflection of the glass I noticed Maureen take something out of her pocket and put it into her bag. It wasn't so much the action itself but the furtive manner in which she went about it. Before going off home again, she decided to go to the toilet, leaving her bag on the kitchen bench. Something operating at an intuitive level, as well as plain old curiosity, made me want to look in her bag. On opening it, there on top was a fat bundle of well-worn £20 notes. My heart sank. *Not Mum's savings! Surely not robbed by her own daughter!*

I was so shocked I forgot to close the bag, and when Maureen came out of the bathroom she could see from my expression and from her opened bag that the game was up.

'So, it's been *you* taking the money all that time, letting Mum think it was Laura?'

She never answered. She just stood there looking like a naughty schoolgirl.

'How could you do that? Stealing from your own mother's savings. That's got its own special label that has; it's called elder abuse.'

Maureen took her bag and sat down on the couch, staring ahead but saying nothing. After a while she admitted that yes it was her, but tried to justify it by the way Mum had treated her. Every time she was treated poorly, it cost Mum £100. For any real put-downs or deliberately nasty comments, it was £500. Over the years, it had added up to over £5,000 worth of hurt.

'So, that's how you paid for your facelift, then?'

'That was my way of coping with all the crap over the years, all her meanness and her malice. So, I just balanced the books the only way I could.' She looked at me and closed her bag.

'What are you gonna do? Call the police?'

'No... but I want you to stay until Mum wakes up and then go in there and very graciously accept her apology. I want you to hold her hand and allow her the time to open up and say what she wants to say to you. Will you do that?' Looking sheepish, she nodded that she would. I felt an urge to hug her and to hit her at the same time, but I did neither.

'Do any of the others know what you've been doing?'

'I think Colleen suspects cos I gave her some money for the animals. I called it charity money.'

'What about Eileen, does she know?'

'God no. You know how holier than thou she is. You've no idea what a temptation it's been. All that miserliness, me getting sent all over the place to save a penny here and there, no heating being put on, not allowed to flush the toilet for a pee or to run a bath, and she had all those thousands of pounds hidden away. And for what? It was doing no good for anyone where it was, just building up while she spent hours every week counting it. All them bundles of twenty pound notes just stuffed away.'

'Where's it hidden?'

'In the bottom of her wardrobe in a cardboard box.'

Poor Mum. What poverty and deprivation she must have suffered during her earlier years to have felt the need to go through her old age still trying to keep herself safe from starvation.

A sound of groaning was coming from the bedroom.

Mum had woken up. So, without any delay, I ushered Maureen in there, but this time I stayed too.

'Mum, Maureen's here. She's come to see you.' She looked at Maureen and smiled weakly. I nodded for Maureen to take her hand and hold it, which she did.

'How are you feeling?' Maureen asked her, looking at me and then back at Mum. Mum just gazed at her before finally answering that she didn't think she'd have long to go now and that she had something she wanted to say.

'I just want yer to know that I regret how I've been. The way I've treated yer, it wasn't good. I don't know why I was like that, but I'm sorry… Can yer forgive me?' Mum's voice was small and shaky. I don't think she'd ever said anything like that before to anybody in her entire life.

I didn't need to prompt Maureen anymore. She was crying and sobbing, saying yes, of course she forgave her, and asking if Mum could forgive her. She didn't say what it was that required forgiveness and Mum didn't ask. By this time I too was tearful as Mum and Maureen emotionally connected in a positive way with each other. Mum gently patting the shoulder of her youngest daughter, comforting her 'pretty little baby' who was lying down next to her again. Our precious lives. What an unbridled mess we can make of it all!

* * *

The following day, Mum didn't want anything to eat, not even a morsel of jam tart, just small sips of tea. She was like a living skeleton lying on the bed and there didn't seem to be anything I could do to alleviate her suffering. Even though the morning sun was shining through the window, I asked her if she'd like to go for a Saturday night dance at The Grafton one last time. Surprisingly enough, she agreed. Making her as comfortable as possible in the bed, I turned on the familiar music and prompted the images that would create the scene in Mum's mind. But when I asked if she could see herself being held by John Thornton, she weakly shook her head and said in a little whispering voice, 'No, it's not him.'

Intrigued by this change in the usual imagery, I asked, 'Who is it, Mum? Who are you dancing with?'

As the music played on she seemed to drift off to sleep, but then she said, 'It's your dad… He can dance lovely now.' On hearing this I was really taken aback and couldn't think of anything to say. Mum continued to speak. Her voice was so low I had to bend my ear over her mouth to hear what she was saying.

'He said he's been having lessons while he's been away… but he's back now to take me home.'

Mum's face looked very peaceful and contented. She just lay there barely moving. I stared down at her, feeling a little frightened by what I'd heard. I didn't know whether to turn off the music to bring her back to reality or not, but as the next track on the CD began playing a waltz we didn't usually listen to, I quickly pressed the stop button. Leaning over Mum, I listened to make sure that she was still breathing. She was, but it had changed. Instead of continual breathing in and out, she would stop and then after a few seconds start again. I quickly rang Julie to see if she could call in as soon as possible to check on Mum. She said she'd try to be there in about an hour.

While waiting for Julie I sat on the end of Mum's bed and watched her. She wasn't responding at all when I spoke. If Mum's death was going to be like this, then for her it was nothing to be frightened of. But it was harrowing for me, the waiting and watching. I tried to engage in mindfulness to help myself stay in that precious moment, to be there with Mum while she was still alive. I half wished she'd sit up and demand a boiled egg, or anything.

The nurse finally arrived and, although I would normally have left the room to allow Mum some privacy, this time I stayed while Julie examined her.

'It won't be long now,' Julie said in a low voice. Hearing those words made me feel instantly cold inside as they conveyed the awful realisation that my dear mum was about to disappear forever.

'I think you'd better let the family know. If anybody wants to say goodbye they should come as soon as they can,' she added.

Going into the lounge I tried to phone my sisters, but my shaking fingers were all over the place, clumsily pressing the wrong numbers while my mind kept going blank. On finally making contact with Colleen, I asked her to phone the others and tell them they should get over here right away because this time it really was happening.

When I returned to Mum's bedroom, the nurse was shaking her head as she told me that Mum had already 'gone'. Although it was a blessing that she'd been granted her wish to go peacefully with no pain, at that moment I was engulfed by a tsunami of emotional pain. How strange it was to feel so shocked and to be in so much anguish although her death was expected and even hoped for given the suffering she'd been experiencing. Most of all, I felt a huge sense of loss. I'd been at hand, yet I hadn't even said goodbye. But I was grateful Mum had died not knowing who'd been pilfering her money and that her request to apologise to her youngest daughter had been granted.

Later that day, my sisters and I, along with two undertakers, escorted Mum into the lift one last time. There was a sense of the surreal as Mum's body, which was in a body-bag and strapped to a stretcher, was placed upright in the lift standing alongside her daughters. She remained in that vertical position, held by the undertakers, as the lift descended to the ground floor. It was a truly awful and macabre sight, totally undignified, but the lift wasn't wide enough for the stretcher to be horizontal.

On the Death Certificate the cause of death was simply put as Old Age. We never really knew if Mum had bowel cancer or not. Although she did have several symptoms of that disease, she didn't have enough to warrant a certain diagnosis and, being so old and frail, a colonoscopy or exploratory surgery had been out of the question.

That evening I stayed with Colleen as I didn't want to go back to Mum's flat on my own. There were a lot of things to organise, such as the funeral, sorting out Mum's belongings and bank accounts, putting a notice in the Deaths column of the *Liverpool Echo* and informing the appropriate government departments that her council flat would now be available for another elderly person. That night I went to bed feeling emotionally wrung out. All the necessary jobs would have to wait until tomorrow and be shared amongst us.

* * *

The next day, after helping my sisters with the tasks at hand, I returned to Mum's flat with Maureen. As there wasn't much there any of us wanted to keep, we'd brought several large cardboard boxes to fill for the Jospice (St Joseph's Hospice). I wondered if Milly on the ninth floor would like something, but after the unpleasant incident with her son I didn't fancy going up there.

Maureen referred to Mum's death using the euphemistic term 'passing' and seemed uncomfortable when hearing me saying words such as 'death' and 'dead'. I suppose *passing* has connotations of leaving one place to arrive somewhere else, a continuing journey, whereas *dead* sounds more final, the end of the journey. I noticed that even Julie referred to Mum's death as her having *gone*. These more sensitive descriptions probably sound less harsh for the newly bereaved, but death is a reality, just as being born is a reality, both of these being 'the immensities' as Mum described them.

Removing Mum's clothes from the old wire hangers in her wardrobe was enough to set me off weeping again. At the bottom of the wardrobe under a pile of old cardies was a cardboard box full of the birthday cards, Christmas cards and Mother's Day cards I'd sent her for every year I'd been away. The New Zealand calendars were also there in the same box, all in consecutive order from the earliest to the latest. How hard it must have been for her, despite our weekly one-hour phone conversations, to have her firstborn living at the other end of the earth. And how sad it was to think that, back in Auckland, in a wardrobe in my house lay a similar box containing 36 years' worth of cards *From across the miles* and all the Liverpool calendars I'd received from Mum and my sisters. What a way for us to have lived our lives! But becoming caught up in how things could or should have been is futile. Such thinking can only create unhelpful feelings of regret, anger or guilt.

Maureen directed me to what lay in the other corner of Mum's wardrobe. Hidden beneath a mountain of old shoes and slippers was another cardboard box, this one filled with bundles of twenty pound notes. Maureen told me about the dream she'd had that previous night. In this dream, Mum came to her saying she was understanding about the money and forgave her. That she loved her. It was certainly a good example of how the subconscious mind can find ways of helping out a troubled conscious mind.

Along with the savings from her pension was Mum's horse-racing wins. Most of the money had been accumulated over the years by her going without and buying only the cheapest of items. This cache of banknotes became known as Mum's 'starvation money', and according to her will it was to be shared equally amongst her four daughters along with some money in her ISA bank account. If only Mum could have spent it on herself instead. Such thoughts were coming thick and fast and it was Maureen who reminded me that Mum always had very basic needs and often said she had everything she wanted in the way of material things. However, a cruise would probably have been a wonderful experience for her while she still had some physical independence.

The next task involved collecting all Mum's little treasures that she'd kept over the years, all the gifts given to her by family members who had travelled overseas: a blue and white ceramic windmill from the Netherlands, a red Flamenco fan from Spain, a couple of stuffed toys, including a kiwi from New Zealand and a koala from Australia. Mum's treasure trove also included some of the prizes she'd won on the bingo when she used to be a regular player. Most of these were tawdry junk, but there was one item that stood out as being worthy of keeping. This was a set of little liqueur glasses with a range of hunting scenes painted on them. I remember when Mum won those glasses during an afternoon bingo session and they had remained in their box unused all those years. As children we'd get them down from the high shelf in the parlour and study the pictures on them, which included horses and dogs and aristocratic looking men in their hunting attire. A painted world so far removed from our working class environment in Canal Street.

After spending the morning sorting out Mum's belongings, Maureen went back to Warrington while I stayed at the flat. Everywhere I looked reminded me that Mum was no longer alive. My spirit, psyche, or however you want to describe that inner essence of a human being, felt crushed with grief. On the radio, a song called *Moonlight Shadow* was playing. Was Mum now existing in some other dimension or was she just a dead body without any form of continuation? I felt an urgent need to get outside and go for a walk. To have a look around my home city of Liverpool.

Walking through Bootle, I came to the place where I used to go to school in Irlam Road. Saint Mary's Primary School was long gone. This area not far from the docks used to be a hive of activity in the late 1950s. Large Clydesdale draught horses with hairy feet were used to pull carts of sawn logs along to the Dock Road. From all directions, there were dockers on their bikes shouting out, 'Ow are yer?' to each other as they cycled past but nobody ever seemed to wait for a reply. This greeting of 'Ow are yer?' was spoken so fast, it sounded as though they were saying 'Iya'.

One day, as a child standing by the school gate, I remember listening intently to the variety of sounds coming from the docks. Men's voices, ships' horns, the thumping noise of heavy cargo being loaded off and loaded on to boats. The clatter of dock life. But now, the place was desolate. As I walked along, there wasn't a soul anywhere and all the big brick warehouses of the past stood empty and unused like giant gravestones, remainders of Bootle's past importance as an industrial hub. No longer having to rush back to look after Mum, I caught a bus from Stanley Road into Liverpool Central.

To me, the city of Liverpool is uniquely interesting. There's the magnificent architecture of the Walkers' Art Gallery, Saint George's Hall and the city's two great cathedrals. Walking down to the Pier Head, I inhaled the familiar salty smell of the River Mersey. Sailing on the ferry across this river and back again reminded me of a time when hundreds of people used this mode of transport for a family day out to New Brighton. Looking out across the river from Wallasey, I could see the Royal Liver Building's two towers, their two giant liver birds perched on top. Instead of going back to Mum's flat, I caught a train at Central Station to Eileen's house in Crosby.

Although Liverpool is an impressive city full of grand architecture and maritime history, it's the people who live there that make it such a special place. Standing at the bus stop on Stanley Road or while travelling on the bus or train, there was this natural camaraderie between people. On the whole, Liverpudlians tend to be very friendly, often engaging in good-natured conversation sprinkled with humour. On the bus and on the train, people readily offered their seats to the elderly, to pregnant women or to those with young children. When asked for directions, strangers would go out of their way to be helpful. If they didn't know, they would ask others who might. It all represented a very people-focused culture. The only other city where I've experienced this level of good-natured friendliness is Dublin. But then there are many people of Irish descent in Liverpool, and at one time Liverpool was jokingly known as being the capital of Ireland.

By the time I arrived at Eileen's house I was feeling a little better than how I'd been at Mum's flat earlier that day. We still had to organise somebody to take all Mum's furniture away as a "job lot" but most of the usual tasks associated with a death had been completed. A date for the funeral at Saint John's Church was set for the following Wednesday. It was real then. Mum had finally died. But there was still a sense of disbelief, as though I could easily wake up from this long dream and there she would be waiting for her tea and toast.

Eileen was not told about Maureen stealing the money and the subject was never raised again between any of us. Of all of us, Eileen seemed the least upset by her mother's death. Perhaps her strong Christian faith gave her something to cling to during such sad times. Also, the fact that Mum had acquiesced to the religious pressure placed on her would have created a sense of relief for Eileen. Colleen and Maureen's beliefs leaned more towards a general spirituality. They believed that Mum was now in the spirit world along with everybody else who had "passed". Looking back at that particular time in my life, I wish I'd also had some sort of faith to lean on, such was my psychological neediness for comfort. I didn't even care if it was true or not. But just when I was willing to suspend all discriminating thought processes, the rational part of me shook its head in disgust, asking if I'd also like to believe in Santa Claus or perhaps the Tooth Fairy because they too might provide some psychological consolation.

I hadn't yet told my sisters what Mum's last words had been about Dad arriving to take her home. From a rational viewpoint, Mum was embracing the power of her imagination, just as she had with all the mind-dancing over the last few months. Yet from another perspective, she was being helped across to the Other Side by her late husband. Once again, rational and irrational views came face to face, both offering conflicting powers of persuasion.

The dining table in Eileen's house was set for three. James had prepared another chicken meal which was very similar to the one I'd enjoyed last time. This time, however, I allowed him to keep refilling my wine glass, hopeful that alcohol would help ease the heartache. As usual, Eileen drank only fruit juice, refusing to even have a taste of the wine.

The conversation at the table moved from recent property prices in Crosby to whether or not Planet Earth would survive another twenty years due to global warming. James said he was happy to continue being a hedonist, enjoying good food and wine. As an afterthought he included art and dogs. He didn't seem to care much about anything else, not even mentioning Eileen or his family. From Eileen's perspective, if the world did end within twenty years, then that would be God's decision and the start of the long awaited Apocalypse, heralding in the Second Coming.

People say that opposites are supposed to attract, but I couldn't help pondering on how James and Eileen ever came to be a couple. I'd never encountered two people so unlike each other. But then, as the French say, 'Vive la difference'!

After the meal, we went for a walk along Crosby beach with the dogs. At sunset, it was quite eerie seeing all the iron men sculptures by Antony Gormley standing naked along the beach. Having drank three glasses of wine with my meal, I still felt no better emotionally. In fact, I felt worse. Alcohol seemed to highlight rather than dull the sense of sadness and poignancy around a beach at sunset. I could hear James and Eileen talking as they walked in front of me, but their voices sounded a long way away.

Using the cognitive behavioural tools of my trade, I tried to reframe unhelpful thoughts to something more positive. Mum was now out of her misery and, who knows, maybe I would see her again one day. If that wasn't the case, then I could be grateful for the opportunity to have spent the last remaining months of her life getting to know her and caring for her. Yes, it could be a win-win situation if I could just reframe my thoughts. Regardless of my efforts at cognitive restructuring, hot tears continued to trickle down my face as we walked back to the house. I gently reminded myself that grief is a natural response to losing a loved one. It is not a disorder.

16

Dressed in an embroidered blue and white silk nightgown, her body lay in an open coffin in the funeral parlour. Somebody had painted red lipstick on her mouth (which had smudged) and caked rouge on her cheeks, thus producing a garish and unnatural appearance. Her hands lay across her chest, hands the same size and shape as my own.

While looking at Mum's corpse, the one question screaming for an answer was – where had *she*, the essence of Mum, gone? Bending down, I kissed her body's cold forehead and touched her hand. My three sisters stood next to me, each of us gazing down upon our dead mother. But unlike them, I wasn't able to contain my grief. It was as though her death had unleashed all the pent-up sadness and despair imparted from my thousands of clients over the last few decades. Grief poured out of me like a river, bubbling up from its source in my heart until I was a snotting, sobbing and uncontrollable heaving mess. As a therapist I'd tried to help my grieving clients by describing the pain of bereavement as being the price we pay for loving others. No wonder people from all over the world create a variety of religious beliefs to provide some sense of comfort to ease this terrible pain. Seeing the dead body of somebody you love calls for help beyond earthly shores.

On the day of the funeral it was raining. Apart from her four daughters, James and Daniel, and a couple of Mum's elderly neighbours, there was nobody else at Saint John's Church that day other than the priest in his robes and the hired pall-bearers. I had hoped Laura, Brenda or Julie would be there but, given the nature of their jobs, I suppose there would be too many funerals for them to attend.

We wanted the service to be a musical event as Mum always loved music so much. It was planned by us, her daughters, as though she would be there in spirit, watching our efforts like the Queen watching the Royal Variety Performance. The old black and white photo of our parents on their wedding day was placed on the coffin facing the congregation. Looking at the photo, the same old questions around life and death invaded my mind. Would our parents now be together again in spirit, or are they just two lifeless organisms decomposing along with all the other dead creatures on the planet? I really was struggling between the immensities, trying to understand the alpha and omega of life.

In keeping with her theatrical flair, Eileen wore a large black fur hat, looking as though she'd scored a starring role in *Doctor Zhivago*. She sat on the left of the front row along with James and Colleen, while Maureen, Daniel and I sat on the right with the two neighbours. Such a tiny congregation to be sitting in a huge empty old church.

The service began with the priest saying something in Latin. He then spoke about Mum, how she was baptised at this very church and attended Saint John's School as a child. He spoke about her time during the war, particularly the May Blitz and the destruction of the air-raid shelter which had occurred only a short distance from the church. This was followed by the CD tracks we'd selected, beginning with *Lara's Theme*, one of Mum's many favourites. It had been chosen by Eileen, which had probably influenced her decision to wear the fur hat, or maybe it was the other way round! On hearing this beautiful music, I realised what a mistake it was to play it so early on in the service as it immediately turned on an emotional tap.

Maureen wanted to sing a song for Mum, so after *Lara's Theme* she stood up front by the priest and sang *The Last Rose of Summer*. She had a pleasant folksy sort of voice and the words of the song were exactly how Mum often described herself as being – *The last rose of summer left blooming alone, all her lovely companions are faded and gone.* How Maureen could sing that song without breaking down, I don't know. Perhaps that's how a spiritual belief can ease the sadness of bereavement, a gentle balm to help relieve a stinging pain. Mum would have appreciated Maureen's performance, if she was there to hear it.

When the time came for me to stand up front and speak, I had to waive the opportunity. I could hardly breathe let alone talk, thanks to the emotional consequence of the music. Colleen too was a casualty of the music. Her face was covered by a hanky as she tried to control her loud spontaneous sobbing. With hindsight we should have had the speaking first and then the music. The last musical track to be played was *Danube Waves*, the waltz that Mum liked to dance to in her imagination. As I listened, in my mind I saw her dancing around a ballroom with Dad. They were both younger and full of energy as they waltzed to the music, looking very happy to be with each other.

If there's one thing more painful than seeing the dead body of a loved one lying in a coffin, it's seeing that wooden box being lowered into the ground knowing the person you love is inside it. What a strange thing to do, putting somebody under the cold dark earth. She was buried on top of our dad's coffin in the same grave. Standing around the open grave, Eileen could see Colleen and me starting to emotionally dissolve again, and in her own way she attempted to rescue the situation by getting a bit of humour going. Impersonating Dad's voice as the coffin was lowered into the grave she called out, 'All these bloody years waiting here for yer! Where the hell have yer been? What kept yer so long?' Laughing and crying at the same time seemed to relieve the built-up tension. I could just imagine Mum saying to Eileen in a pseudo-serious whispering voice, 'Ooh God, don't say that,' before roaring with laughter herself.

We left the cemetery before the workmen had finished filling in the open grave and travelled back to Eileen's house for ham sandwiches and an assortment of cakes. Mum had specifically requested that she be 'buried with ham and cakes'!

* * *

A few days after the funeral I kept my promise to Mum by lighting a candle for her in Saint John's Church. During the funeral service I was so focused on wondering where she had gone, I didn't take much notice of the church itself. Its dark and majestic interior created a sombre and intimidating atmosphere. Seeing the candle I lit flickering against this imposing backdrop certainly provided a sense that something meaningful was taking place, something that was sure to attract the attention of God. I prayed my simple prayer – if there was any God or higher power that could hear me, a power that valued love, kindness and compassion, then I would like to make a request. My request was this – if there is such a thing as a soul, that my mum's soul would be happy and free from harm wherever she'd gone. If there was no such power and no souls, then Mum would be okay anyway as it would mean she hadn't gone anywhere, she'd just be a body under the ground. I could see how a simple act such as lighting a candle in a church for a loved one, whether they be alive or dead, could provide an element of comfort for the person doing it. I sat for a while pondering on how fragile we humans are with our emotional need for rites and rituals to mark life's milestones.

On my way out of the church the priest walked over to me. He'd known Mum for years and spoke highly of her – what a good Catholic she'd been and how proud of her I should be. I was proud of her, but not for the reason the priest was suggesting. She'd survived a hard life. She'd known extreme poverty and war, and she had remained loyal to her husband and children when we needed her more than she needed us. Quietly nodding at the priest's words, I walked out of the dim cavernous building into the bright sunlit day.

Once the cost of the funeral and other expenses were met, we divided Mum's "starvation money" into four. The amount came to just under £4,000 each. I accepted my share with a heavy heart as most of it was in cash, emphasising the fact that Mum had needlessly continued to live just above the poverty line all those years of her old age. Buying the engagement ring seemed to be the only time she'd ever really treated herself and even that was from a second-hand shop. Maureen accepted her quarter of the money without there being any objections, the theft having been quietly forgotten.

Eileen spent her inheritance upgrading her car, even though she already had a perfectly good, nearly new vehicle. Colleen had her house painted and bought a new fridge. Maureen put her share in the bank 'for now', using the interest to boost her wages. And as for me, I didn't know what to do with mine. Booking a cruise appealed simply because Mum had said she would have liked to have experienced that, but none of my sisters wanted to accompany me despite my offer to pay for them. Perhaps that was why Mum never went on a cruise; there was nobody who wanted to join her. If only she could have suggested it to me. I like to think I'd have come over in a flash and even been excited about sharing a cruise with her. But like many elderly people, she probably didn't want to put anybody to such trouble.

The longer I considered it, the more enticing the idea of a cruise became, but who could I go with? I wondered about Milly up on level nine with her ulcerated leg. Perhaps she'd welcome being treated to a week away on a cruise ship. But Milly was no longer there. When I knocked on the door, another elderly woman opened it. She didn't know what had happened to Milly, but claimed that she was now the new tenant. The janitor looking after the flats told me that Milly had gone into a care home a few weeks ago. He gave me the address of the place so I could track her down, which I did.

Milly was pleased to see me. She'd recently undergone a hip operation after having a fall and was now recuperating in the care home. She was shocked to hear about Mum dying and had a little cry. She was also apologetic over her son's aggressive behaviour towards me that last time we'd met. It was Arthur's idea that she should now leave her flat and move into this home on a permanent basis, but, according to Milly, as soon as her hip mended, she would be returning to her flat. I didn't have the heart to tell her that somebody else had already moved in there.

'Have you managed to keep up any of the relaxation meditation or imagery?' I asked.

Milly shook her head. 'No, love, I haven't. Arthur took the music things when he thought it was all to do with being hypnotised. You see, love, he couldn't bear to think I was enjoying myself.'

This Arthur really was a nasty character. I asked Milly if she'd like to come on a cruise with me. That I'd treat her out of Mum's money and we could go away for about a week. She could go in a wheelchair if need be, and with medical staff on board she'd be well looked after. We could share a cabin with a balcony and sail around the Mediterranean, maybe even going ashore to places like Rome or Athens.

Hearing myself saying all this, I realised what I was doing. I was using Milly as a substitute for Mum.

Milly looked astonished as she took in what she'd been offered. But when she spoke, it was to say no, she couldn't come because of her health. She thanked me for thinking of her, but it wasn't just her hip, it was her leg too. I wondered if it might also be something to do with Arthur. If he wouldn't allow her to listen to 'hypnotising' music, there would be no way in the world he'd allow her to go for an overseas holiday with the wicked hypnotist. I was disappointed but realised it was probably best for Milly if she stayed where she was.

A few weeks after the funeral, my sisters and I paid a visit to the cemetery to wish Mum a happy birthday. At last she had her own little bit of land, the tiny garden she'd always wanted, but how sad that it had to be a cemetery plot. We each brought some flowers to put on her grave. It seemed a bit awkward bringing flowers for Mum, not only because she never appreciated them, but our dad was also under the ground in this spot and he had never been acknowledged by any of us all the time he'd been there. We were, however, all quite young when Dad died and, although he was loved in a very general way, we'd lacked the maturity to appreciate the depth of our loss. The impact of Mum's death on us was hugely different. We were now all middle-aged women and Mum had been "one of us" for a long time.

As we knelt down to arrange the flowers on the grave, the old family humour started up again. This time it was Colleen. She was impersonating Mum's voice shouting her disapproval of the flowers, 'Take them away!' and 'Take them back; don't waste yer money!' This time we were laughing without crying.

Looking around at the surrounding gravestones, it was strange to read that many had died during the May Blitz in 1941. It was likely that some of them had lost their lives in the Bootle air-raid shelter. With Mum now gone, there wasn't anybody left alive to recall the terrors of that night.

While staying over at Colleen's house, I awoke suddenly from my sleep, still feeling the sense of anguish from a dream that seemed to have gone on for hours. In the dream I was back in our old house in Canal Street waiting for Mum to return from the shops or wherever it was that she'd gone. I kept going to the front door and peering up and down the street to see if I could see her in the distance walking towards our house. As she'd been out all afternoon, I was worried that something untoward had happened, that maybe she'd met with an accident.

As the afternoon wore on, the sky became darker and it began to rain, lightly at first and then heavily. Every few minutes I was getting up and checking at the front door, but there was still no sign of her anywhere. The street was lit by an old gas lamp on the corner, its dim light revealing the falling rain and the emptiness of the street. She'd been gone for hours. I was worried about her frailty and how low her energy levels would be after all this time away. She would be suffering. It was when I began to cry while standing at the door, whimpering into the street, 'Mum, where are you?' that I woke up. There were no tears on my face but I could feel the tension of the dream in my body, along with the lingering heartache.

17

Having nobody to accompany me on a cruise, I decided to go by myself. I liked the idea of sailing on one of the Cunard cruise ships because of that shipping line's historic association with Liverpool. Of all Cunard's available holidays, a Mediterranean cruise on the *Queen Victoria* appealed the most as it involved sailing to some of the Greek islands in the Aegean Sea and disembarking at Athens. I'd always been interested in Greek mythology so, for me, this particular cruise seemed the most suitable. In some ways I half entertained the idea that Mum would be coming with me in spirit, no doubt such fantasising being a result of some underlying guilt on my part and an attempt to make up for all my years of absence.

Cunard's *Queen Victoria* is one of the most beautiful of cruise ships. The opulence of the grand lobby is breath-taking, something I imagined Buckingham Palace to be like. Initially, I thought the people on board might be la-de-da and perhaps look down on the likes of me because of my Liverpool accent, but they weren't like that at all. There was a variety of Northern accents, including those of Liverpudlians, and most people were polite and friendly towards each other. There were even some Australians and New Zealanders on board who I instantly warmed to. Along with middle-aged couples, many of the passengers were older women, either travelling together or alone, and you could be as social or as private as you wanted to be. Yes, Mum would have loved it all right, maybe even more than the Blackpool lights!

Because many of the women had no male partners, yet enjoyed ballroom dancing, the ship's staff included some male dance partners who were available for any female passengers wanting to dance. Although these immaculately dressed mature men were known as Gentlemen Hosts, in my mind they were Silver Foxes. I thought what a wonderful thing for Cunard to provide such a service as many of the women enjoyed their evening waltzes and foxtrots with these dashing men, whom I observed to be excellent dancers. Being in such high demand every evening on the dance floor, they must have gone to bed exhausted at around midnight each night!

While on board the ship I enrolled for dancing lessons, which were free for any interested passengers. My goal was to dance with a Silver Fox in the main ballroom before disembarking at Athens. Having mastered a foxtrot, I sat alone at a table one evening near the dance floor, waiting. Very soon one of the men approached and politely asked if I would 'Care to dance?' in such a refined voice. Being held by a man who knew how to lead a woman around the dance floor was a very pleasant experience. At last I could understand why Mum had enjoyed dancing with John Thornton so much.

My cabin had a balcony attached so I could sit there looking out to sea as the ship sailed along. The water was mostly calm and the air temperature warm. Gazing up at the clear star-filled night sky, I would whisper, 'Where are you, Mum? Where have you gone? Can you hear me down here?' Even though she wasn't physically with me, I felt a sense of closeness to her. As I was the only one of her daughters whose fingers were thin enough to fit her engagement ring, it was now on my middle finger, and of course became a constant reminder of her. There was also the fact that the cruise itself had been paid for with Mum's savings.

The holiday wasn't all plain sailing though as it included some bizarre and inexplicable incidents. It started one afternoon when I lay down on the bed in my cabin hoping to have a nap. I was about to drift off to sleep when I felt the distinct sensation of somebody very gently sitting down on the end of my bed. When I looked up to see who it was, there was nobody there. Just a few seconds after laying my head back on the pillow, I felt it again. It was as though somebody was trying to be very gentle so as not to disturb me. Lying there focusing on what was happening, I knew I was wide awake and that I could definitely feel the weight of whatever it was slowly shifting about at the end of my bed.

Part of me was scared because it's so unnatural to feel some form of life moving on your bed yet with nothing being there. The other part of me was curious in a scientific kind of way as the movement continued. It felt like a cat making itself comfortable in slow motion in the hope it wouldn't be chased off the bed. After a few minutes I was convinced that somebody must be in the cabin with me, playing a joke, or worse. I quickly got up and checked under the bed. But there were only my suitcases there. I looked in the wardrobe, in the bathroom and on the balcony. I even looked over the balcony to make sure it wasn't somebody from the next cabin, but nobody was there.

Feeling confused and afraid, I left my room and went to one of the dining areas on the ship to have a cup of tea while I attempted to analyse what had just happened. I knew about the types of phenomena that could happen during sleep, the hypnagogic and hypnopompic hallucinations. It's possible that because I was actually drifting off to sleep the first time I felt the movement on the bed, I may have been in that transitional state between wakefulness and sleep. However, the second time I experienced it was after looking up to see who was there, and I knew I wasn't asleep then.

Drawing on my psychological training and experience for an explanation, I wondered if it could simply be due to my own highly emotional state after losing Mum. I'd had bereaved clients tell me about seeing their departed loved ones, hearing them, feeling their presence and even experiencing certain smells that couldn't be rationally explained. Perhaps our own psyches come to the rescue in conjuring up a scenario that might provide some element of comfort for an aching heart. It seemed strange for me to attempt a self-analysis of what might be described as a psychosis – experiencing something that doesn't exist in reality. In other words, was I coming face to face with my own madness?

There was, of course, the other explanation. That it was something to do with the paranormal, something that couldn't be understood via objective reasoning. Perhaps it really was Mum answering my question, letting me know she was still around in spirit and that she was OK. Naturally, it would have been easy for me to jump to that conclusion when taking into account my level of emotional neediness at that time and my craving for some indication that she continued to exist. But I would imagine a spirit to weigh nothing, and what I experienced seemed to involve a light weight shifting about.

So, there I was again, in that state of not knowing, struggling to understand this mysterious phenomenon we call death but not really getting anywhere. I decided the best thing I could do to help myself come to terms with my mother's death was to create a ritual that would provide some sense of closure. A final farewell involving a little last supper on the balcony drinking the Babycham I'd brought with me. But what to eat? It could only be a scallop butty. On *Queen Victoria*, scallop butties were not on the à la carte menus, so I made a special request of the kitchen manager for one of the chefs to slice some peeled potatoes and throw them into the chip-pan for me when they were cooking chips, which he was happy to oblige. The passengers on board were always treated as being very important and no request ever seemed to be too much trouble.

A slice of white buttered bread was easy enough to obtain, and so I took my fried scalloped potatoes and piece of bread back to my cabin. The balcony table was set for the feast. Opening a bottle of Babycham, I poured the fizzy liquid into a flute glass and celebrated being alive and the fact that I was on this fabulous cruise. I raised my glass 'To my dear mum, wherever you are' and 'Wherever that is, may you be happy and safe.' By the time all the little bottles were empty and the scallop butty eaten, I felt the best I had in a long time. The sea was blue, the breeze was warm and life was good. That night I slept soundly.

The next morning the ship anchored off the island of Santorini. After a half-day excursion to this beautiful island, I relaxed on my balcony with a gin and tonic. The Aegean Sea was the most vivid azure blue I'd ever seen. Looking across at Santorini I was struck by the beauty of the island, how white the buildings were, with some of the roofs being the same vivid blue as the sea. These were the colours of Mum's diamond and sapphire engagement ring which sparkled in the sun as I slid it off my finger. Holding the ring in my hand I wondered about throwing it into these waters as a farewell ritual. Instead of wishing that Mum was actually with me on this cruise, I began to believe it would be more constructive if I focused on the memory of her life rather than on where she might be now that she was dead.

I leaned over the balcony railing to cast the ring into the sea but changed my mind at the last second. This ring now symbolised my connection to Mum. Being there on my hand each time I looked down maintained my memory of her. Would this be a morbid way to live? No. It was all to do with love. I imagined what she'd say if she could see that I was about to throw her ring into the sea: 'Ooh God, don't do that! It cost a lot of money that did.' I stepped back from the railing and sat down. Putting the ring back on my finger I slowly finished off the gin and tonic.

On the last day of my cruise, I disembarked at Piraeus in the morning and caught a taxi to Athens where I'd booked a night in a hotel before flying back to the UK. After visiting the Acropolis, I went to the National Archaeological Museum where I spent the whole afternoon. I loved looking at the beautiful marble statues dating back thousands of years, especially the females in their robes and sandals. Their lovely faces reminded me of Mum when she was young.

That night as I lay down on the bed in my hotel room in Athens, it happened again. I was very much awake as I felt the definite sensation of somebody gently sitting down on the end of the bed near my feet. Looking up in the semi-darkness of the room, I couldn't see anybody there. Turning on the bedside lamp, once again I got up and checked all around me, under the bed and in the bathroom and wardrobe, but there was nobody in the room. Leaving the lamp on, I climbed back into bed and lay on my side, my heart beating fast and my breathing shallow. After a short while I felt the same movement again, the gentle positioning of a weight at the end of the bed. It brought back a memory of Mum coming in to see me when I was a child, sick in bed with the measles. Back then, it felt gentle and loving, just as it did now. I wished I wasn't so frightened. If it was Mum's spirit, then surely that should be a comforting thing. But it was more distressing than anything.

This time, though, I decided to stay in the bed and try to monitor second by second what was happening. Slowly but surely, the sensation of movement, with slight hesitations in between, began to shift upwards. I could feel it moving by degrees along the side of the bed from where my feet lay, up towards my back. I knew I was wide awake and feeling the definite sensation of something being there, something moving very close by. I just lay stiff as a log, my heart beating as fast and as loud as a metronome at high speed.

But it was all too much. I sat up and called out loud, 'Go away! If it's you, Mum, thank you for letting me know that you're still around, but please don't do this to me because it's frightening me too much.' I lay down again, breathing rapidly with the fear of what was happening and from the shock of what I'd just heard myself saying. Finally, sitting up in the bed, I whispered, 'I love you, Mum, and I always will. May God bless you… and goodbye for now.'

Although I didn't feel the strange movement anymore that night, I didn't sleep. At 2am I was sitting at the table having a cup of coffee. I had the TV on with the volume turned low so as not to disturb other hotel guests. At long last the grey light of morning arrived. As soon as I finished my breakfast, I ordered a taxi to the airport and checked out early from the hotel even though my flight wouldn't be taking off until late afternoon.

Looking back, it was an unusual holiday and had taken an unexpected turn. The irony of the situation is that I'd got what I'd always wanted – a personal experience that would provide me with enough assurance to believe there is something more to us than simply being biological accidents having no continuation once we're dead. At a personal level, I accepted that it really was Mum letting me know she was still existing in some way. But from a scientific viewpoint, one individual feeling an unexplained movement on a bed would hardly count as evidence of anything significant apart from the psychological state of the person experiencing it. But *I* was that person and what had happened over the course of that holiday was enough to create an important shift in my world.

I remembered my conversation with Colleen about the blue light and the other bizarre incidents she'd experienced. Was this really any different because now it was me experiencing such inexplicable phenomena? Just as Colleen 'knew it for sure' that she wasn't imagining it, I also felt the same way. According to a psychiatric diagnosis, I was experiencing a psychotic episode involving "transient tactile hallucinations" following the emotional turmoil of a bereavement. All I knew was that what I'd experienced had been enough to move me from being an agnostic and not knowing whether there was or wasn't anything to believe in of a spiritual nature, to being a believer in something, even though I didn't know what that something was. I was pretty certain, and still am, that I didn't imagine it. But where do you go with such a problem? Who do you turn to after having had such experiences? If it were to do with my hearing, I'd go to an audiologist. For my sight, an optometrist. But what about paranormal tactile visitations? Who specialises in those? I wondered about seeing a spiritualist when I returned to Liverpool. Perhaps my mind would now be more open and less sceptical, and no doubt, Maureen could recommend a 'really good one'.

On returning to the UK, Eileen and James met me at the

airport and drove me back to their house. When I told them what I'd experienced four times in two different beds, they remained silent while they took in what they were hearing. When they spoke, I was given two very different and rather surprising viewpoints. Eileen's advice was that I make an appointment to see a psychiatrist before returning to New Zealand! James admitted that he'd experienced something similar when his grandmother had died. He was 22 at the time and not particularly close to her, nor was he that upset over her death. But one day soon after the funeral, he saw her very clearly sitting in a chair in his mother's house. When he looked again, she was gone. He said it hadn't bothered him in the slightest. He believed that what I'd experienced was just Mum letting me know that she was OK – 'So, she's still here, still hanging about!' James concluded. 'Quite within character really.'

It was a blessing for me to hear James say that. Maybe I shouldn't have let the experience frighten me. To try heeding that same advice I'd offered Colleen – to just feel loved and comforted by what was happening. But that would have been very difficult, especially given my training in psychology in which this sort of phenomenon comes with its own set of labels. But how could "transient hallucinations" brought on by the grief of bereavement explain James seeing his grandmother when he wasn't even grieving?

I wasn't sure if I should tell Colleen about the strange incidents, as she might still be feeling a bit fragile in regard to her own paranormal experiences. And given Maureen's proclivity for calling in priests and their ilk to exorcise haunted houses, I decided not to mention it to her either, at least not for now.

* * *

Before booking my flight back to New Zealand, I went to see Milly in the care home. I had a few little presents for her, one being a souvenir from Santorini and the others being Mum's CD player plus her CD of the waltzes. Milly was really pleased with her gifts although she admitted to being a bit worried about Arthur.

'He might not like it, love, the music thing. You see, he's got it in his head that I was away with the fairies and it wasn't good for me.' I didn't want Milly getting off side with Arthur because, as bad as he was, he was her only relative.

'Well, how about we give them to the matron to look after for you?' I suggested. 'You wouldn't have to tell Arthur about it.' Milly didn't look too convinced about that being a good idea.

In the care home lounge, there were about a dozen elderly people sitting in armchairs, most of them were women and many were staring at me while I spoke to Milly. I noticed there were lots of walking sticks, crutches and walkers about. What a life, I thought. They're probably just waiting for the next meal to arrive so they have something to do. Milly must have noticed my expression as I looked around the room. 'I bet a lot of them would enjoy a night out dancing,' she said, with a faint smile, 'you know, a last waltz.'

Milly's comment gave me an idea. Why not provide the means for these poor old souls to engage in dancing imagery?

If it could bring Mum a lot of pleasure at her late stage of life, then why wouldn't it work here? Besides, I didn't really want to go back to New Zealand just yet and I knew Colleen would be glad for me to stay at her place for a while longer as she still didn't like being alone at night.

So, off I went to see the matron of the home, explaining to her how group meditation followed by dancing imagery to music would likely bring a lot of pleasure and physical benefits to many of the residents. That it would be a bit like recreational music therapy and, as I was a registered psychologist, there shouldn't be any concerns around me being qualified enough to do this as voluntary work. To my pleasant surprise, the matron thought it was a great idea as long as I provided the music.

Milly was overjoyed when I returned to tell her I would be allowed to offer "music therapy" there every Tuesday and Thursday mornings. She was so pleased about what I'd organised she even entertained the idea of staying in the care home rather than trying to return to her flat in Marsh Lane.

I too was pleased. It was an opportunity to brighten up the mundane existence of these people – my new "clients". To hopefully bring a sense of joy back into their lives via meditation, music and mind-dancing. Yes, in a very short time that old Grafton dance hall would be a hive of activity again, its dozen or so new members spinning about the dance floor like there was no tomorrow. And maybe, just maybe, there are endless tomorrows!

About the Author

As well as being a writer, Dr Doreen Davy works as a registered psychologist in New Zealand. *Between the Immensities* was inspired by true events and is her third published book.